The Affliction of
ADDICTION

The Affliction of

ADDICTION

It's Not That Complicated

(Science Answers *All* Questions)

Adam McArnold

Welcome to an Exciting
Evolution in Treatment & Recovery

AFFLICTION –
"The <u>cause</u> of persistent
pain or distress
– great suffering"
– Merriam-Webster (2000)

The Affliction of

ADDICTION

It's Not That Complicated

Beliefs about various causes of addiction impact treatment effectiveness and recovery. The beliefs of where addictions stem from affect many areas of clinical treatment, from how information is interpreted to how clients are perceived and how treatment is applied. These beliefs affect:

- What addiction is
- How addictions develop
- Motivational tactics
- Treatment approaches
- What is needed for recovery
- What constitutes recovery
- The stigma of addiction
- Professional conduct

Adam McArnold

The Affliction of Addiction:
It's Not That Complicated (Science Answers All Questions)
Published by Pen Pal Press
P.O. Box 617
Canandaigua, NY 14424

The Affliction of Addiction: It's Not That Complicated (Science Answers All Questions) Adam McArnold

Cover design by Nick Zelinger of NZ Designs

ISBN: 978-0-692-61450-1

PSYCHOLOGY / Psychopathology / Addiction

FOR PURCHASES, INQUIRIES, and COMMENTS: please visit TheAfflictionofAddiction.com.

Canandaigua, NY

Pen Pal Press

Dedication

I would like to dedicate this book to John and Patty, two of my long lost friends; two of whom rest in peace among the millions of others who have fallen victim to this most treacherous, torturous, and insidious illness; two of whom may still be among us had they been able to grasp the serious reality of their condition, and an understanding that is completely free of all the guilt, shame and remorse that brought them to such despair. So, in honor of all those who have fallen, I have written this book to tell others it does not have to end like this. There is another way out.

Contents

Items of Interest

❧

WHAT CAUSES
ADDICTION?

---

and...
DOES IT MATTER?

NO

What really matters is what
people & professionals
"BELIEVE"

Author's Suggestions

This book examines the impact that causal perceptions have on addiction, treatment, and recovery.

Because of the repetitive nature of this topic, this may be a book that is best read and understood over the course of time, rather than reading it through from cover to cover as one might read a classic novel. This of course will take an adequate amount of time to ingest and absorb.

The concepts presented within are novel and may be quite new to most people. Therefore, I recommend taking time in between chapters to question everything; research the claims, discuss what you find with others, and re-read anything you find to be confusing. Consequently, reading one or two chapters per week may be the best way to get the most out of *The Affliction of Addiction*. I hope this will be for you, as it has been for me, an adventure of enlightenment and hope. Thank you.

Preface

What is addiction? How does a person become addicted to a chemical substance, and what is needed to fully recover from its bondage? This book will provide insight into the causal factors of addiction, thereby helping to reduce all the confusion and biased opinions that plague not only the public's perception, but that may also lie in the minds of all who desire to be of help. It is my hope that the information in this book will help us arrest the progression of addiction much sooner than ever thought possible, and in so doing relieve the suffering of those affected by the addictions of others.

This book is unique. Having spent many years studying addiction, I can say with complete confidence that there is no educational program that teaches anyone how to take all the potential "Models of Addiction" (theories) and put them into a usefully effective format; a comprehensive synthesis of all the research. Basically, all students and professionals are left on their own to develop their own understanding, which undoubtedly includes their own experience with alcohol and drugs. This leads to a wide range of ideas and the use of axiom-driven norms that are not based in science, but rather on individual experience and human logic. And, logically speaking, addiction will probably always appear to be a *self-induced* mental disorder stemming from the *willfully excessive* use of a psychotropic substance. This socially accepted conceptualization of addiction is a huge barrier to effective treatment. Instead of building up one's self-esteem and confidence, it only serves to tear a person down. This sends addicts right back into the use of their drug for the relief and comfort they know they can find in it. However, it does not have to be like this.

We now have undeniable evidence that not only do drugs affect people differently, but that the brains of some individuals are more affected by the use of some substances than others and these are the people who develop chemical addictions.

This information requires that we reevaluate how we think about, explain, and treat chemical addictions; it may even be our ethical responsibility to do so. The term *genetic predisposition* is not a reference to impaired psychological functioning, as so many have suggested or implied, but rather it refers to actual biological differences in response to various psychotropic substances, a *biological reaction*. So, how do we incorporate this information into our current understandings of addiction? This is what this book is all about. We will explore how prevalent the psychological and sociological understandings of addiction are in the field, how detrimental and limiting these one-sided perspectives are, and how beneficial it may be to acknowledge and effectively apply our new biological evidence.

With any change comes resistance. There will probably be some who will scoff at what I am presenting; however, I suspect that there will be plenty more who will suck it up with great thirst. There may also be some who will find some parts more useful than others. To this, I urge everyone to take what they can and leave the rest. The information I am presenting here has not been dreamed up out of thin air. It comes from twenty years of experience, empirical evidence, and most importantly, the experts themselves; those who have successfully recovered from a seemingly "...hopeless condition of mind and body" (Alcoholics Anonymous, 2001, p.20), a chemical addiction.

For the purpose of simplification I will be using the word *addict* to refer to any chemically dependent person, regardless of which drug is involved, including alcohol. In using this word for this purpose, I am not labeling those who have an addiction as their condition, nor is it meant to imply any disrespect. We all know that people are much more than any condition they may have. When I make a reference to a chemically addicted person as an addict I am merely making a reference to those who have addictions. There is a big difference between *calling* a person an addict, in passing judgment, and *referring* to those with addictions as addicts, meaning those who are addicted. Disrespect comes into play when the word addict is used in a derogatory and demeaning manner, and I would expect all of those reading this book to understand this highly controversial and most important distinction.

I will also be using the term *addiction* to refer to the "desire-to-use," as this is the tangible part of addiction. Obviously, there is more to it, but that does not mean it is as complicated as it has been made out to be. It is actually quite simple once we understand the how and why of it. The hard part is trying to understand why only some people fall into addiction while others do not. The answer to this question is also quite simple, but it may take an open mind that is free from all the clutter of previously held beliefs. Therefore, some may need to unlearn what they think they know about addiction before they can fully understand and accept what this new evidence is telling us. Consequently, I have chosen to challenge currently held beliefs in Part One before I delve into the application of this new research in Part Two.

In this era of high technology I can envision great strides of improvement in the field of addiction, primarily in treatment and prevention. The 21st century may be a very exciting time for the field, or it may continue to be filled with endless controversy and confusion. It all depends on how well we can accept, adapt to, and incorporate our new discoveries. Here we are taking the first steps in reaching new horizons of more effective and efficient treatment.

IT'S TIME TO
QUESTION
WHY WE BELIEVE
WHAT WE BELIEVE

PART ONE

A Call for Change

INSIGHT -
"The act or result of
apprehending the inner
nature of things"
- Merriam-Webster (2000)

Chapter 1

Introduction

Causation can be a highly controversial subject; however, one *fact* I think we can all agree upon is that (for whatever reasons), drugs cause addiction; for without them, addiction is not even possible. Therefore, it is the "for whatever reasons" that cause so much confusion and controversy in the field – and in the minds of people everywhere. New discoveries inform us that the widely held perception that everyone is biologically susceptible to addiction appears to be a fallacy. In fact, we now have some pretty strong evidence suggesting only some people are. These are the people who are much more vulnerable to both the *effects* and *adaptations* that can come from the use of various substances.

This rather new information, which is something I will be elaborating on in detail, holds the potential to have a huge and profound impact on prevention and treatment effectiveness.

However, well-established theories and beliefs of the past are standing in the way of its proper utilization. One such theory is the unfounded belief that causation is irrelevant. This, unlike theories based in scientific study, is merely a belief, which by the way, might only be a coping mechanism for the profession; a way to avoid the conflict between all the psychological beliefs about addiction and the new scientific evidence we now have. Therefore, in this era of advanced scientific discovery, this issue of causation is of paramount importance. Please join me on this adventure of enlightenment, hope, change and reform.

It is through our scientific discoveries that we can gain a much greater understanding of addiction; how it starts, progresses, and eventually takes over one's thoughts, will, and actions. This is the intent of this book – to provide a *conceptual understanding* of addiction that works; an understanding rooted in science and directly derived from research studies and scientific experiments. It is also, I might add, something the field of addiction has never had before – a conceptualization of addiction capable of explaining all the mysterious and perplexing questions that have plagued the field of addiction for centuries. All other theories fall short, which is why there is so much confusion in the field. For example, it is not enough to inform children that using at such a young age will cause addiction later in life, for even they know this does not hold true for everyone. They need honest answers and now we have them to give. As you may find, the simple truth can be most empowering.

Today, technical advancements have made it possible to peek inside the brain and measure specific chemical and structural differences that only appear in people who become addicted to chemical substances. For example, while under the influence of alcohol, serotonin levels are different between alcoholics and non-alcoholics. Also, scientists now have the ability to measure, down to one half of a centimeter, structural changes occurring directly from the use of chemical substances. This appears to account for, or at least contribute to, the progression of addiction in some people. It also appears that these biological changes do not occur at the same rate in all people, even when the same amounts of a substance are consumed. It is becoming more and more obvious that some people, if not most, are more *resistant* to these types of drug related neurological changes. Therefore *only* those who are more susceptible to neurological changes develop chemical addictions, and the degree to which one is vulnerable to these changes lies in one's uniquely individual biological reaction to a specific chemical substance.

Because of these findings, biological differences in people can no longer be ignored. According to a statement by Dr. Nora Volkow, the Director of The National Institute of Drug Abuse (NIDA), biological predisposition may account for 40-60 percent of the reason why some people develop an addiction and others do not. Meaning, other factors such as psychological and social factors would account for the other 40-60 percent. This tells us there are some biologically vulnerable people who may never develop an addiction, but it also strongly suggests that only those who are biologically vulnerable in the first place could develop an addiction. This puts a whole new light on how we think about causation.

With findings like this, it is getting harder and harder to negate the profound impact biological factors have on addiction. They have the ability to affect how people perceive those with chemical addictions; and thus, hold the potential to have a huge impact on the recovery process for all those afflicted. However, they might only be useful if our biological information is used accurately and not distorted by preconceived notions, beliefs, and norms; which, as I will be presenting in the following chapters, is a very real threat to the best possible use of this information.

Never before have we had so much scientific evidence to help us uncover the mysteries of addiction, yet most of it still remains unused. It appears the field of treatment has become the guardian of this information, selectively deciding which evidence to present or suppress according to individual and collective belief systems. This leaves the ones most in need of it, those afflicted, out in the cold and having to rely on the belief systems of those providing treatment. And, if an addict's personal experience with a substance does not coincide with the information they receive in treatment, this disconnect could be what leads so many to relapse. In order for addicts to recover from addiction, they need to develop some very strong rock-solid beliefs about their condition. So, if some information is being purposely and selectively withheld, the addict's causational options to believe in will be limited. And, if they don't come to believe in any causes, *they cannot avoid them* and relapse becomes the most likely outcome. This is why addicts must believe in a cause if they are ever going to recover completely. Otherwise, they will be stuck "in-recovery" indefinitely.

Out of curiosity, I asked many addicts who were recently discharged from 28 days of inpatient treatment, these two questions: <u>What is addiction?</u> And, <u>What causes it?</u> To my astonishment, most of them replied, "I don't know." And when I asked them if they thought they had an addiction, most of them replied, "I don't think so, I'm not as bad as, or like, those other people in treatment." Needless to say, I found their answers to be most disturbing. How can anyone fight off, or even treat, a condition if they do not know what it is, or whether or not they have one? Should this not be where treatment starts?

In exploring these "I don't know" responses, some clients had elaborate life-story explanations for why they turned to alcohol and drugs. Others blamed their addiction on family problems or past traumas. Some blamed their addiction on their own mental failings. And still others had a whole array of explanations and rationale, but none of them – not a single one – dared to place any blame on the drug they loved to use, their *drug of addiction*. With all the evidence we have today, I found their answers to be pathetically shallow, as if they had all been rehearsed or just repeating what they had heard. Every explanation was clearly tainted with some degree of blame, shame, or guilt. This is when I realized that not very much has changed over the years. In some subtle or implied way all these patients were being taught that they were in some way responsible for creating their own addictions, and this has not changed for hundreds of years.

Addicts have many reasons for using chemical substances; however, none of these clients were attributing any degree of blame to the actual drug they were addicted to, or to their very own and uniquely different biological reaction. This is when it became obvious to me that these clients were actually picking up on and procuring the causational beliefs of their treatment providers. And since they were continuing to relapse, this was not working out very well for them. As you will find, some beliefs are more effective than others.

Today, with all our new scientific evidence, I am confident we can release our addicts from all the guilt and shame we have been indirectly imposing upon them. The psychosocial approach of blaming self and/or others may have been effective for those who could accept this blame, but it is quite obvious that it does not help the majority. In fact, it has probably contributed to more relapse than we are willing to acknowledge.

Therefore, through numerous examples, I hope to make it plainly clear just how much of an impact causational beliefs have on treatment and the recovery process. Some of this may appear rather harsh and offensive to the profession; however, this is not my intent. I merely want to emphasize a need for change, and to do so, I must expose currently held perceptions, attitudes, beliefs, and norms that not only hinder treatment, but appear to be standing in the way of progress.

Please take note: chemical addictions are not the same thing as process addictions. Process addictions are also referred to as behavioral addictions and include gambling, sex, food, as well as other obsessive compulsive disorders. These disorders may share some of the same cognitive (thinking) processes as chemical addictions; however, they do not involve the impact of psychotropic substances on the brain, nor the damage they can cause. This is why chemical addictions are a completely different monster. Chemical addictions are driven, at least in part, by the effects of drugs on the brain, process addictions are not.

I would also like to add that the issue of causation is only one aspect of the whole recovery process. However, it is an essential part of effective treatment. Causation is what addicts can build their recovery on, but only if they come to *believe* in an actual cause. If treatment providers do not believe in the biological cause of addiction, neither will any of their patients. After all, they are the professionals. All patients and professionals have a *belief* in what they think causes addiction, and no matter what it is, if their belief is weak, tattered, or frayed, it will inevitably crumble.

The biological perspective addresses this problem by providing addicts with a solid and unwavering explanation; that they have *a biological condition – a biological reaction to a specific substance that will never change.* It is this knowledge, along with neurological repair from abstinence and psychological rehabilitation in therapy that eventually eradicates addiction. Some may achieve this freedom and overcome their addiction completely, and others may not; however, it has become very clear that addicts need something to believe in that cannot be shaken, rationalized, or denied if they are ever going to gain any real amount of freedom from the call of their drug. This is the difference between finding recovery and being in recovery, which is another topic I will be covering later in much greater detail. Full and complete recovery is not only achievable, it is the *relief* that every person with an addiction is searching for whether they realize it or not.

Since everyone holds an idea or belief on causation, beliefs are going to be a part of the recovery process whether they are acknowledged and addressed or not. If they are not addressed or are presented in a way that is indecisive, such as referring to the cause as it may be this or that (or any number of possibilities), this will only confuse those in treatment and hinder their progress in recovery. All people with chemical addictions must develop some pretty rock-solid beliefs in order to recover. They must not only know why they became addicted to a chemical substance in the first place (so they can avoid it in the future), they must also know *why* they can never use again like other people they may know. And, they must become okay with this. They must develop a *belief* strong enough to do battle with the drug that has such a powerful hold on them; the drug they love to use so much. Therefore, any explanation must ring true to the person being treated, not the treatment provider.

If the causational beliefs of the treatment provider do not match and coincide with the experience of those being treated, it can create a huge chasm between the counselor and client. According to Brickman and associates (1982), bringing the issue of whom or what is responsible for problems and solutions into awareness leads to improved therapy. If the counselor and client differ on either one of these issues, openly or indirectly, they will be at odds on how to work together; thus, not much can be accomplished. In most cases, clients struggle to believe what their counselor believes, which is probably due to the vague and persistent incongruence between the addicts' actual experience and the beliefs of those being imposed upon them. This may even account for why we have not seen very much, if any, improvement in treatment effectiveness for decades, despite all our other advancements, such as the use of more recent evidence-based therapies (i.e., CBT, DBT, MI, etc.). The point here is that everyone has an opinion on what causes addiction, and whatever that opinion is, it will always be present in treatment efforts.

Most people and treatment providers do not believe in any single cause of addiction. However, let us look further into the available scientific evidence and the impact causational beliefs have on the delivery of treatment and the recovery process. To start with, let's take a quick look at how genetic predisposition may be responsible for the different *effects* and different *adaptations* found in those with addictions.

Epigenetics, which means above, or in addition to, genetics, proposes that the development of various diseases are the result of not one, but multiple genes (gene-sets) that do not interact with their environment very well. This concept is based on all the genetic research gained over the past few decades and is providing us with a whole new way of understanding and treating chronic illnesses, such as diabetes, heart disease, and even chemical addictions. Through the use of technological advancements it has become apparent that the interaction between environment and genetic makeup is quite individually unique. Environment plays a much greater role in the development of chronic illness than previously thought. These environments include physical (such as various drugs), psychological and social stress factors. This explains why some people are more prone to addiction than others, even when ingesting the same quantities of the same substance. It can explain why genetic predisposition appears to skip generations and why some siblings may be more prone to addiction even though they all come from the same parents (Bland, 2011; Bland, 2008; Epigenetics, 2008).

For example, conditions such as heart disease are considered to be the result of eating too much fat-ridden food. However, not everyone who eats foods high in saturated fat is equally susceptible to heart disease. In other words, one person's expression of their uniquely different set of genes may be heart disease from ingesting too much fat-ridden food, whereas, another's may be joint pain from ingesting too much gluten, such as what can occur in people with celiac disease (CD). Applying this concept to addiction can explain why one person would be more susceptible to addiction than another; such as in the way some brains are more affected by them. And, why some people can be rather immune to the same substances to which others become addicted.

This makes a lot of sense and it may just provide us with a very important clue as to why current treatment approaches are not working very well. For example, people with celiac disease (CD) who experience joint pain inflammation from gluten should stay away from foods high in gluten in order to keep this biological reaction at bay. Likewise, those who experience extreme effects and/or neurological adaptations from the use of alcohol and other drugs should avoid them as well. The point here is that unless the person with CD knows that it is the gluten in the food that is responsible for causing their pain, which they see others ingesting without harm, they are unlikely to remove gluten from their diet. They must be *told* it is the gluten in their food that is causing these outbreaks. And, more importantly, they must *believe* in this truth if they are going to comply with such abstinence. In the same way, people with an idiosyncratic response to the same drugs others ingest with immunity are not likely to stay away from them either. That is, not unless they are informed. They must *be told* what has caused their reaction (their addiction) – their biological response. They experience different reactions, such as hunger for more while using, and their inability to avoid use during times of stress. And, just like the CD patient, they must *believe* they are affected differently by the substance than other people. This is hard for anyone to accept, especially for those who have been led into believing that their obsessive use is due to a multitude of other factors such as poor mental health, a using attitude, past traumas, or any other such logical explanation.

The single greatest barrier to recovery for any addict is the acceptance of being different, especially if the addict is led into believing it is all in their heads - a psychological weakness. Most any addict, especially those in early addiction and new to treatment, will fight off any psychological explanation for addiction with everything they have. This is normal; this is a protection of the psychological self. However, considering all the new biological evidence we have today, how much easier will it be for addicts to accept the fact that it is really the drug that causes addiction rather than any psychological failings? Yes, much easier. We know that psychological and social factors also play a role in the development of addiction; however, there is a huge difference between *development* and actual *causation*. This will become abundantly clear as we continue on, but first I want to emphasize how important this biological factor is; a factor that is virtually and completely ignored in most treatment efforts today.

For example, while discussing the topic of biological causation with others in the field, I have heard all too often that causation is not a concern for them. They say they do not treat the cause; they diagnose and treat the condition, the symptoms. This is why we must unlearn what we think we know, to make room for new information.

Over the course of many years and through an increase in governing bodies regulating treatment protocols for patients, the field of addiction treatment has become very safe, stagnant, and methodical. Treatment now reaches only those who have been severely affected, which are usually the clients who have been in and out of treatment for many years. Such long-term and often ineffective treatment creates the perception that one must *want* recovery; that they must reach their lowest point before they can recover; before they are willing to give up their addiction. This is commonly known as "hitting bottom."

What I am proposing – what the acceptance of biological causation can accomplish – is that addicts will not have to sink to such low levels of despair before they can be reached.

All they really need is an acceptable explanation for why they can no longer use and this can be accomplished through education and the acceptance of biological vulnerability. This holds the potential for much faster recovery times and improved treatment outcomes.

Douglas Quenqua, in *Rethinking Addiction's Roots and its Treatment,* informs us that the American Board of Addiction Medicine (ABAM), which was founded in 2007, was offering accreditation to at least 10 medical schools in 2011. Today that number has risen to 39 schools. This is a direct result of all the scientific evidence that has accumulated over the past 20 years or so. In this article Quenqua writes, "Central to the understanding of addiction as a *physical ailment* is the *belief* that treatment must be continuing in order to avoid relapse" (Quenqua, 2011). This article is a good indication of how the medical field is starting to embrace our new biological evidence, but it also makes one wonder why the field of addiction continues to resist the biological components of addiction with such fervent skepticism.

Obviously, the biological components of addiction must be pretty sound for medical schools to be taking such a strong hold of them and referring to addiction as a *physical ailment*. However, the full benefit of these acknowledgements has not been readily accepted, or put to use in the field. Previously held beliefs involving psychological and social causal factors appear to be standing in the way. Because most clinicians have already heard of genetics playing a role in addiction - and tucked this information away as rather meaningless – in light of the fact that genes alone cannot determine addiction (all or nothing), as new biological discoveries arise, they are not even looked at anymore. The result of this response to biological evidence is that newly acquired knowledge is outright ignored, distorted, or misapplied, apparently in a misguided attempt to fit biological factors into psychological explanations; clearly, an attempt to bolster long-standing beliefs. One of these beliefs has to do with recovery, and it stems from the well-accepted axiom, "Once an addict, always an addict" which, as you will come to learn, is only a half-truth. The truth is, an addict is only an addict when they are addicted.

When Prochaska & DiClemente (1984) wrote the *Stages of Change* they included a last stage of change called "The Termination Phase." This phase states that a change has in fact occurred; that the amount of effort and diligence put into maintaining a change is no longer required. This theory applies to addiction as well as any other change. However, this phase is practically nonexistent in the practice of treatment today, not because it does not apply to addiction but because it is *believed* not to apply. This is likely due to the fact that so many recovering addicts, in and out of treatment, do relapse.

However, when we understand what addiction is and what causes it, we can begin to understand that addiction can be completely eradicated.

The addictive response to the drug is permanent; this is what is responsible for all the biological, psychological, and sociological adaptations that drive addicts to keep on using. However, the end result, the addiction, can be completely eradicated when all the driving forces behind one's desire-to-use have been extinguished.

In other words, with abstinence, the biological source of the addiction is removed, and eventually the biological urges to keep on using dissipate and disappear over time. However, all the psychosocial *adaptations* that have occurred from use remain. It is all the psychosocial adaptations from the use that keep addicts returning to the source of their addiction, even after years of abstinence if they are not addressed and overcome. So, in essence, once an addiction has developed, the psychosocial adaptations of addiction are just as destructive as the biological cause. However, it is important to understand that these psychosocial adaptations can be eradicated through abstinence and therapy. Therefore, if one's biological reaction to a substance causes addiction in the first place, then this is what it will always do. This is powerful information for an addict - the knowledge that the biological response to a substance (the actual cause) is permanent; and that the addiction, all the biopsychosocial adaptations that occur from the use of a substance, are not permanent.

Therefore, and contrary to the popular belief that all addicts must work at maintaining their recovery indefinitely, many people have actually *recovered* from their addiction – they no longer have the *desire-to-use*. They have fully accepted their biological condition in which they respond to the use of a substance more profoundly than others, and actually prefer sober living and clear thinking. Apparently, this concept of full and complete recovery has been discarded as a way of playing it safe, or a misconception of where chemical addictions actually stem from. If addictions stem from the psyche, then a healthier psyche would have to be *maintained* (in-recovery) for the rest of one's life. However, if addiction stems from the drug, as the evidence indicates, and the use of the drug has been extinguished, then all the psyche would really need is a lot of *repair and readjustment* in order to fully recover (thus, recovered). We must realize that addiction does not come from the mind, like so many well-intentioned people believe, teach, and insinuate, but that it comes from the effects of a drug on the brains of those susceptible to adaptations (similar to joint pain emanating from gluten in those people susceptible to the effects of gluten).

Today we have all the evidence we need to provide addicts with biological explanations for their chemical addictions. This, in turn, provides them with a sound belief system upon which they can build a solid, stable, and lasting sobriety. I call this giving them a *foundation* upon which to build a permanent recovery; it is giving them the knowledge – that for them to use, because of their own biological reaction, they would always fall right back into addiction. This is why addicts are powerless over addiction; they are powerless over what the drug does to them. It is beyond their control. They cannot control how their brain is affected by some chemicals. Knowing this removes any and all hope of ever being able to use safely, like other people. It is this stark reality of their condition that allows them to recover completely. They cannot change their biological reaction, but having it does not make them an addict. According to the belief of psychological impairment causing addiction, one would be doomed to a life of practicing recovery on a day to day basis; always being in recovery and at risk for relapse instead of obtaining recovery. *Recovered* addicts know why they cannot use. Those *in recovery* live in fear of their mental and spiritual ability to remain sober. The information contained in this book will clarify this difference for many and provide hope for those seeking a permanent solution.

Treating addiction and being effective at it are two very different things. The fact is, causational beliefs impact treatment and recovery; and, they will continue to do so regardless of whether or not this reality is ever acknowledged. Surely, it is better to challenge our own preconceived beliefs and notions rather than to remain in our well-accepted static mode of norms and axioms, especially in a field that has undergone numerous changes in theories, techniques, and approaches, but has yet to realize any significant gains in terms of improvement.

"We See Things
Not As They Are
But As We Are"
- H.M. Tomlinson

Chapter 2

A Call for Change

With 12 month relapse rates ranging anywhere from 80-90 percent, can anyone really be satisfied with how effective the treatment of addiction is today? (Hendershot, C., Witkiewitz, K., George, W., & Marlatt, A., 2011) Yes, we have come a long way since the 1950's regarding how much blame we put upon the individual and in understanding how the human mind works, but is this the best we can hope for? How much longer can we continue to blame these poor results on the intricate dynamics of addiction and not look at how much of an impact our own views of addiction may have on these poor results? We can do much better.

How much better is yet to be discovered; however, in a fairly recent pilot study by Schuckit, Kalmijn, Smith, Saunders & Fromme (2012), making use of our biological evidence has shown to reduce the consumption of alcohol in vulnerable college students, specifically those with a high tolerance to alcohol. These are the students more likely to develop an addiction because they are the ones who consume more (remember, it is the drug that causes addiction). Therefore, high tolerance is one indication of a higher biologic vulnerability. High tolerance alone does not determine whether a person will become addicted or not, but this is one of the first experiments to make use of biologic differences as a treatment intervention.

In this study, the experimental group was informed of this simple fact (that high tolerance is associated with the development of alcoholism), while this information was withheld from the control group. This was the only difference in an otherwise identical intervention given to both groups. Those of the experimental group who had genetic markers for high tolerance consumed less than those in the control group with genetic markers for high tolerance. This was a rather small experiment, but it did suggest that the mere knowledge of one's biological vulnerability could be fairly effective in prevention efforts. The significance of this study lies not so much in the use of different *effects* (high tolerance), which is a milestone in its own right, but it demonstrated how much of an impact this knowledge can have on treatment effectiveness, as it allows clients to *believe*.

The important thing about this study is that it may very well be an impetus for similar studies based on biological differences. As it stands, addiction has been viewed as some type of mental inferiority for centuries and centuries. With the growing body of evidence that reinforces biological predisposition as the actual cause of addiction, there is also a growing separation in beliefs. Beliefs are not quite the same as perceptions. Two people can perceive the evidence the same, but only one might believe in what the evidence is suggesting. Those more accepting of our biological evidence are starting to view chemical addictions as an idiosyncratic (abnormal) reaction to use; whereas those more grounded in a psychological viewpoint are continuing to attribute addictions to psychosocial factors.

Both perspectives play a role in the *development* of addiction, but not necessarily the *cause* of addiction. This is an important distinction to remember: chemical addictions cannot develop without some degree of biological predisposition to a particular substance. In other words, evidence is showing us that psychosocial factors cannot cause addiction in anyone without some degree of biologic vulnerability. Higher *degrees* of biological vulnerability indicate higher degrees of risk for addiction.

BELIEFS

Beliefs are what this book is all about. There is no question that causal beliefs affect and impact how addiction is perceived and treatment is applied. Thousands of years ago addiction was blamed on the rebelliousness and sins of ones' parents. Roman soldiers hunted down and killed physically abnormal newborns just days after their birth for fear the children were possessed by demons, and drunkards were believed to be possessed by demons as well. Even as late as the 1700's, severe alcoholics were placed into insane asylums where they were tortured in an attempt to scare the demons out of them. And, even though the use of torture as a "treatment" for addiction had ceased by the 1800's, the practice of committing alcoholics and addicts to psychiatric institutions continued on well into the 1900's (Rubin & Roessler, 2008).

These reactions clearly demonstrate that the *fear of causation* existed in previous societies. We believe we are beyond this fear today; however, we may not be all that advanced.

This fear remains in the unfounded belief that mentally healthy people can avoid addiction. In other words, this is why we tend to believe all people can have power over addiction, if they so "choose."

Believing addiction is within the power of the individual is what keeps everyone feeling safe and sound. What is so frightening about the reality of biological predisposition, is that it robs us of our illusion of complete self-control, and leaves us vulnerable to the fate of our genetic propensities. This fear is probably why the acceptance of biological vulnerability has been resisted for as long as it has; why it is continuing to be resisted, even in the face of evidence; and why it has been distorted and manipulated to fit into all our psychological explanations. This is evident in the misguided and misunderstood view of *biological vulnerability,* as to mean or suggest physically *inferior* brains; as opposed to:

Perfectly healthy brains being more affected and impacted by various drugs than other perfectly healthy brains.

Let's not forget about all the smart, famous, and successful people who have fallen victim to what a drug has done to them.

MODELS OF ADDICTION

As most people in the field of addiction know, there are five basic theories on causation. They are called the Models of Addiction. These are known as: (1) the _medical_ or biological cause; (2) the _psychodynamic_ or self-medicating cause; (3) the _social_ or learned behavior cause; (4) the _moral/spiritual_ or anti-social cause; and (5) the _biopsychosocial_ cause, which includes all four of these potential "causes."

I think it is fair to say that the majority of treatment providers today, if not all, would agree that the biopsychosocial model of addiction is the most logical and appropriate one to apply; i.e. each patient may have been affected more by one of these "causes" than another. This perspective of multiple causes makes a lot of sense. However, even among those who believe in this Biopsychosocial Model of Addiction, there appear to be two very distinct and growing separations. Either they believe that addiction stems _primarily_ from psychodynamic, social and moral causes (psychosocial perspective) – or they believe addiction stems _primarily_ from medical/biological causes (biological perspective). These differences are not always made very clear, as they both exist under the clouded terminology of biopsychosocial causation.

For the purpose of ease and clarity I will be referring to these **two causal views** of the BIOPSYCHOSOCIAL MODEL OF ADDICTION as the psychosocial perspective of _causation_, and the biological perspective of _causation_.

Another way of looking at the differences between these two perspectives is through cause and effect, as this may be the main difference between the two. Some people believe that psychological and social factors lead to addiction through voluntary and chosen use, which is very logical (although this does not account for different effects), while others believe that biological factors lead to increased using behavior and mental health problems. The main thing to remember here is that these models of addiction are really nothing more than hypotheses – educated guesses. Nor do they differentiate between actual *cause* and *development*, something I will be elaborating on in much greater detail later.

Therefore, without a clear and universal understanding of where addictions stem from, counselors are left on their own to come up with their own conclusions, all of which place too much emphasis on the behavior of addictive use and what can be done to correct this behavior. This stance creates a huge gap in the recovery process for many patients – *it leaves out any acceptable explanation for why they can never use again.* I have never met a recovered addict who did not have some idea on how or why they became addicted in the first place, and what they choose to believe will affect how stable and secure their recovery will become.

For this reason, most all treatment programs include an educational component that covers these models of addiction. The important thing to remember here is that individual beliefs will bias how this information is presented, and therefore, interpreted. These biases can sway a client's belief toward the biological perspective, the psychosocial perspective, or anywhere in between. And, in most cases, will leave clients utterly confused. It also leaves plenty of room for unintentional biases that reflect the presenter's own beliefs. Whether they are aware of it or not, everyone has an opinion on what they believe is the "real" cause of addiction. The point is, many well intentioned counselors may be unaware of how their own perceptions may be influencing their clients' beliefs, and therefore their potential for recovery. All clients must decide for themselves what caused their addiction; and, unless they are provided with all the evidence, free and clear of any distortion or bias, they can hardly make a well informed and accurate appraisal for themselves. They must decide for themselves what the cause of their addiction was if they are going to be prepared to fight the battle of their lives. Without this, complete recovery is not possible. This may very well be the hardest battle of their life, and unless they have some *cause* to believe in, they are bound to repeat the same mistakes over and over. This is where most treatment efforts fail.

When it comes right down to it, recovery is all about developing some rock solid beliefs, and this takes time. Those with addictions are not only going to have to develop a belief in (1) how and why they became addicted in the first place, but also a belief that: (2) addiction is real, and not all in their heads. Additionally, they must understand (a) what addiction is, so they can know what it is they have to fight; (b) that addictions can be overcome, and that they can overcome theirs; (c) that the only way to overcome an addiction is not to use at all; and, (d) that life can be enjoyable without using. This is a tall order of beliefs, and accepting all of them will be directly impacted by those providing treatment.

Like the issue of biased presentations, other problems have

risen due to the lack of a clear, universal, or definite causation of addiction to believe in. So, the question is, how do we bring these two perspectives together in a more effective, stable, and unified whole? What are the various benefits and pitfalls of each of these two perspectives? And, how does one perspective impact the other?

One example of how the psychosocial perspective can, and often does, impact the biological perspective can be found in an article by Richard A. Friedman, M.D. In it he reports on scientific proof that some people react differently to drugs. This is the basis of the biological perspective. However, his *choice* of words reflects the presence of a psychosocial bias. He writes, "Emerging evidence suggests that drug abuse can be a *developmental* brain disorder, and that people who become addicted are wired differently from those who do not" (Friedman, 2011). He then presents the source of this information to support his statement, which was an experiment conducted by Dr. Nora Volkow. In her experiment she found that people with a high number of D2 dopamine receptors reacted *adversely* to a stimulant she had administered, while those with a low number of these D2 receptors found the stimulant to be *pleasurable*. This is clear evidence that biological differences exist in people and that these differences are most likely responsible for the different *effects* this drug produced in these two groups. This is evidence of biological predisposition. However, let's examine the wording Dr. Friedman used to describe these differences.

In Dr. Friedman's words, an assumption has been made as to *why* there is a difference in the number of D2 receptors between these individuals. The phrase, "developmental brain disorder," creates a very subtle but powerful insinuation, and one that he was probably unaware of himself when he wrote it. By using the words *development* and *disorder*, he insinuates that these differences are not only abnormal, but that having a lower amount of D2 receptors is the result of some disturbance in normal growth; meaning that the differences found in the number of D2 receptors could have been caused by other environmental factors and not necessarily by genetics (being born that way). This is a prime example of how previously held causational beliefs can and will continue to distort new evidence.

This use of words leaves the door wide open to explaining these differences as a result of psychological disturbances, which can cause neurological changes, instead of actual biological predisposition, which has to do with genetics. There are two different implications here: If these differences are developmental then we can assume some control or responsibility, but if these differences are due to genetics, there is no control; there is nowhere to place the blame. The point is, this experiment was not about *why* these differences in type D2 receptors existed, it only showed that they do indeed exist. Any assumption as to why they existed was added by the word *development*. This wording can lead to a lot of confusion when it comes to discussing causation, and it is this type of distortion that hinders the use of biological predisposition by making it sound like it is something it is not. Evidence is often interpreted to fit into the psychosocial belief of causation, whether it is intentional or not.

This is very important to understand because I will be elaborating on the differences between cause (*effects*) and development (*adaptations*) in the following chapters. It also has a lot do with how and why so many treatment providers continue to try and dismiss, by distortion or bias, any possibility of actual biological predisposition (being born that way). We have known for centuries that people react differently to drugs; we just haven't known why until recently. And, thanks to all the experiments like this one, and all the animal experiments that have been conducted over the years, we are on the breaking edge of new and improved treatment.

It may help to understand that if developmental changes could cause some people to become addicts then we could look to a person's upbringing and early life experiences to explain physical changes in the brain; thus providing numerous explanations for higher levels of biological vulnerability. However, if some people are just born with an actual biological predisposition to a chemical substance, we would have to question all our previously held beliefs. We would not only have to rethink all our theories on how and why only some people become addicted, but more importantly, we would have to forfeit our own claim to having control over addiction. This appears to be quite a scary prospect for most of us. So, rather than to outright deny the evidence of genetic predisposition, there has been a growing tendency to manipulate its meaning so that it better fits into our psychological and sociological explanations.

This automatic and natural response to dismiss the possibility of actual genetic predisposition is not going to be easy to address. And, quite possibly, the motivation behind this response is (1) to keep the responsibility for having an addiction on the addict and their life-course circumstances, and (2) that it may stem from our own basic human survival instincts. If some people are born with no control over their addiction, then we must re-evaluate our own claim to having control. According to Yalom & Leszcz (2005), the basic human fear of vulnerability is one of the four basic components of the human experience (the fear of: death, isolation, meaninglessness, and loss of freedom). The loss of the freedom to choose whether or not one uses a substance or not is a most scary, unconscious, and most natural human fear. It is an unconscious fear that resides in all of us, and our professionals in the field are not exempt from it.

This resistance to actual genetic predisposition impedes progress. I had an illuminating discussion with a colleague in the field about Dr. Friedman's article. She is both a college professor and a friend for whom I have the highest respect. She suggested that the lower number of type D2 dopamine receptors found in those who received the pleasurable effects might be the result of environmental stress factors causing biological changes in the brain – such as in the case of a child being raised in an abusive environment. This was her automatic and rather quick response to explaining away actual genetic predisposition. This is my point - this automatic response to the dismissal of genetic predisposition may just be a most natural protective factor, and with no disrespect, a coping mechanism for providers.

Underlying all attempts to dismiss biological predisposition appears to be an assumption that everyone is born with the exact same genes – but only when it comes to the use of psychotropic substances. This is illogical. Here in the U.S. I cannot think of anyone who has not indulged in a drink or two now and then. About 50% of Americans have tried marijuana and millions have tried cocaine and other so-called "recreational drugs." So, nearly everyone has had at least some exposure to them. Most people have experienced over-indulgence or getting drunk at least once or twice in their life. This is why personal experience is probably the single greatest barrier to the full and accurate acceptance of biological predisposition. For, in the words of H.M. Tomlinson, "We see things not as they are, but as we are."

So, what's the point? The point is that addiction is not just a developmental illness, it stems from a biological reaction. I have heard so many people, and well-intentioned counselors alike, state that they themselves could have become an addict or alcoholic had they not had the common sense to put the brakes on their use; that they have had periods in their life where their consumption had gotten out of hand, so they themselves decided to stop or exert more control over their use. In other words, they had to deny themselves. Clearly, they believe addicts do it to themselves; and therefore, should be held accountable. They say it is just a matter of being able to be truthful and honest with themselves.

Well, if it were as simple as this, I wouldn't be writing this book. The truth is, as the evidence shows, everyone is impacted by drugs a little differently. There is no such thing, at least for the biologically vulnerable addict, as willful control over their use. If one has the ability to slow down and exert control over their use, they are not as biologically vulnerable as those who cannot. One can no more make themselves an addict, as they can prevent it. This is because no one can make themselves more or less vulnerable to the effects of a substance. This is determined by something out of our control – our genes. There is not one addict out there who would not love to have the ability to control their use, for this is what they live for – their next use.

If your perception of addiction stems from your own experience with psychotropic drugs, then you might be missing the mark. I am not saying it does no good to slow down and exert some control, for levels of biological vulnerability vary, and drugs do cause addiction. But for those who are highly vulnerable to a specific substance, they cannot control their use. The effects of the substance upon them is what make this type of control virtually impossible. And, for those who believe they have prevented themselves from becoming an addict, they are quite simply not as biologically vulnerable to the substance as those who do become addicted. It is not a matter of higher intellect or better morals, attitudes, stronger willpower, or any such human quality or strength. This is what the evidence shows, and this is what makes chemical addictions so baffling. The only way for highly vulnerable people to prevent addiction is not to use at all, and they can only do this through education and intervention. They must know and accept this truth about themselves if they are ever going to avoid full-blown addiction. The acceptance of the biological perspective holds the potential for very effective prevention programs.

To question and inquire is something to be admired, but, as most would agree, to twist, distort, and use selective information is unprofessional, especially when it comes to this evidence and the potential benefits that biological vulnerability may bring to the field. I have seen how much better the biological perspective can work when it is applied as actual genetic predisposition, and I will be sharing this evidence later on. First, however, I want to further explore how perspectives impact treatment in order to bring awareness to this paramount need for change and how hard this change may be to implement, especially in the minds of those who may not be aware of how strong their underlying beliefs may be.

RESPONSIBILITY –
"Moral, legal, or
mental accountability"
– Merriam-Webster (2000)

Chapter 3

Treatment

All treatment providers understand the absolute necessity of providing patients with empirically supported evidence, facts, and theories about their condition. With the advancements in scientific and genetic research over the past few decades the biological perspective of causation appears to be gaining more and more ground, specifically in terms of applicable use. However, the prevailing perspective in treatment today remains that of the psychosocial perspective.

In most treatment programs today, addiction is viewed and addressed the same way one would address a psychological problem. For instance, take a very depressed, miserable and ornery person who has acquired some very negative and pessimistic attitudes toward life. A psychosocial assessment may reveal a slew of potential causes for such misery. Perhaps this person experienced some very traumatic experiences in life. Maybe this person was taken advantaged of as a child and responded by becoming very selfish and self-preserving. Or, maybe they adopted a perspective that everyone was out for themselves, and they were going to be out for themselves, too. Whatever the reasons for their misery, would they not be the one who is ultimately responsible for their condition? Did they not play a part in causing their own misery? Many would believe so and would insist that they accept responsibility for what they have done, *and are continuing to do to themselves,* if they are going to be helped. This is an "it's not your fault, but it is your fault" way of thinking. In other words, people with mental health problems are not held accountable for what might have happened to them, but they are held accountable for how they *choose* to respond or react. From the words of Yalom & Leszcz (2005),

> Knowingly or unknowingly, the need for taking responsibility underlies nearly every therapeutic intervention. When it comes to psychotherapy, this is rarely, if ever discussed openly and explicitly, but it is the foundation of all psychological treatment. This is usually exhorted through questions like, 'Are you satisfied with the life you have created?'

The use of accountability may be very appropriate for addressing all the psychological problems associated with addiction; however, we have to ask ourselves, is it appropriate for addressing addiction — an addiction that potentially underlies all the psychological problems associated with addiction? Well, only if you believe addiction is a psychological problem, right? However, what if addictions were the product of a biological reaction? Would it still be appropriate? Clearly not. You would you tell, insinuate, or subtly imply that a person with heart disease did it to themselves by the fat-ridden foods they chose to eat over the years. Nor would they need to accept this apparent fact (which, by the way, only applies to those who are vulnerable to heart disease by fat-ridden foods) in order to help them.

In this example, there is no need for an acceptance of causal responsibility because heart disease is not a psychological problem. Once one knows they have heart disease, which, unlike addiction, is clearly evident, they would have to take responsibility for their condition by changing their eating habits. This scenario would be the same for addicts if addiction was viewed and treated as a biological condition. Responsibility would only come into play once the addict accepted their condition. To do this, they would first have to know what addiction was before they could accept it.

This is why so many addicts refuse to believe they are really an addict even after repeated treatment attempts. And, until they can acknowledge their addiction, they cannot take responsibility for having it. The point here is that there is a huge difference between taking responsibility for having a condition and actually causing it. Through the psychosocial perspective of causation this distinction gets lost. And:

Any attempt to motivate addicts into taking responsibility for having an addiction also requires an admission of guilt and shame for having played a part in causing their addiction.

This is a major problem with the current and predominant

use of the psychosocial perspective. However, there is a solution. We all acknowledge that both psychological and biological factors play a role in the *development* and continuation of addiction, but we disagree in which one is the actual underlying *cause* (the old chicken and egg dilemma). This is where it would be very helpful to begin thinking about the biological and psychosocial *causal factors* associated with addiction as two separate entities. This is where we are headed.

Using causal responsibility to correct the mental and emotional problems associated with addiction is both appropriate and necessary. However, to insist that one must take responsibility for causing their addiction is quite inappropriate.

This is because addiction and all the psychological problems commonly associated with addiction are two separate things. They may be intertwined, and psychological problems surely feed the addiction, but they are not one in the same.

In other words, addicts are responsible for their depression, anxieties, fears, low self-esteem, and all the other mental health issues associated with addiction, by the way they think. And, they need to know how they are contributing to these problems in order to overcome them. However, merely overcoming psychological problems will do nothing for the addiction (the desire-to-use), *which is something entirely different.* What addressing them does do, is empower the addict to commence battle with their desire-to-use (their addiction). To think psychological problems are at the root of one's desire-to-use is a common mistake among many in the profession. The truth is, (as you will find in the next chapter) addicts have a desire-to-use when they are happy as well as sad, relaxed or stressed, fearful or safe. It just doesn't matter. What does matter is not to blame the addict for causing this desire-to-use. In fact, just the insinuation that the addict is responsible for causing their addiction is likely to hinder their progress.

Another issue is that of blame, a byproduct of the self-causal belief. Most, if not all, counselors know that clients who suffer from mental distress and addictions are not to be blamed or faulted for having such a condition. However, many of them do not practice what they preach. Many treatment providers today still view addiction as something some people do to themselves. Whether you agree with this objective observation or not, many treatment providers still reinforce this concept of blame, not in overtly obvious ways, for this is clearly not acceptable, but in more subtle ways by blaming the development of addiction *solely* on psychological factors and life-course events. Many continue to suggest that addicts cause their own addiction by not facing their problems in life, making a series of poor choices to use substances, by excessive over-indulgence, and by the simple immaturity of acting irresponsible.

Certainly, a person with a problem must first acknowledge they have a problem before they can be helped. This should be the primary focus for those new to treatment. It may be helpful to remember that addicts may also be harboring those same human fears of vulnerability discussed earlier, which may explain why so many appear to be in denial. Even addicts find it hard to believe they do not have control over their use. There is a huge difference between being responsible for addressing a condition and that of creating one.

A more current view of the psychosocial perspective is that

addicts are viewed as *lacking* in normal cognitive abilities for reasons beyond their control, which is actually a distortion of biological vulnerability. Many who are guided by this perspective attribute one's inability to control their use to acquired attitudes and biologically impaired mental abilities, such as: poor coping skills, lack of self-esteem, immaturity, high impulsivity, low self-control, narcissism, and the list goes on and on. The one thing this perspective does not attribute to biological vulnerability is the different *effects* and *adaptations* produced by drugs in those with addictions, which is really what biological vulnerability is all about.

This newer and more current "no-fault" psychosocial view of addiction produces no better results than that of the purely psychosocial perspective (where the blame is placed on attitude and choice). This is because it requires the acceptance of being mentally inferior – having a brain that is not quite up to par. This does not work because it does not apply to everyone with addictions. Some people with addictions are very successful and talented people, such as all the doctors, lawyers, nurses, and business executives, as well as all the famous musicians and actors who have fallen prey to addiction.

It is no secret that by the time addicts present for treatment, they share a plethora of psychological problems associated with addiction. Some of these issues are likely to be depression, anxiety, anger, resentments, self-pity, low self-esteem, negative attitudes, low stress tolerance, low functionality, etc. However, it is a huge mistake to think, or imply, that these conditions are the cause of addiction. There are far too many people who suffer from these same conditions who never develop a chemical addiction for this "no-fault" psychosocial perspective to hold any weight. And, it is no easier for the person with an addiction to accept than that of being personally responsible.

According to either psychosocial perspective, the discrepancy between improved mental health and the inability to ever use safely again is explained away as the result of biological damage to the brain. This just adds insult to injury. However, this may very well be true. The fact is, we don't know. What we do know is that when biological damage is conveyed as the cause of addiction, the message being sent here is that addicts do it to themselves through overindulgence, as if they could actually control their amount of use and consumption in the first place. This is just another way the psychosocial perspective blames the addict. It is also a manipulation of the evidence and a distortion of the truth because varying degrees of biological *effects* are rarely, if ever, presented with biological damage (*adaptation*). This is why the avoidance of telling patients that different people experience different effects from various drugs appears to be quite intentional. This is a passive reinforcement of the psychosocial perspective. It not only puts the blame on the addict, it also insinuates that anyone who overindulges in any substance will inevitably become an addict, which is a fallacy.

It appears that many counselors withhold this other side of the biological evidence (different *effects*) in an attempt to motivate their clients to change; to scare the addict into changing by showing them pictures of damaged brains (*adaptations*); however, this has no positive effect. We've all heard the adage - "You cannot scare an addict into recovery," and this is very true. Many studies have confirmed this.

As I have mentioned, we know that excessive and extended exposure to psychotropic chemicals causes damage to neurological structures of the brain, which is a very plausible explanation for causation; however, it does not explain why some experience more damage than others, loss-of-control with first use (effects), nor is it something an addict is willing to readily accept without proof that they themselves have encountered brain damage (adaptation). Consequently, they will use again and again until they eventually "hit their bottom." The psychosocial perspective of causation actually perpetuates this response.

Since we know that psychological problems contribute heavily to continued use, these issues need to be addressed regardless of which causal perspective one adheres to. The difference between approaching these issues from the psychosocial perspective versus the biological perspective is that the biological perspective makes no assumption that these issues actually cause addiction. The biological perspective acknowledges that these mental health problems contribute to and fuel continued use, and that these issues are, for all practical purposes, part of the addiction, but they are not necessarily the cause. Mental health will continue to deteriorate and prod more and more use as the addiction grows. Mental health issues, along with the biological deterioration of emotional satiety, in the core structures of the brain, are what drive the progression. However, according to the biological perspective, they are viewed as the result of use rather than the cause.

To sum it up, it may just be too easy for treatment providers to conclude that since psychological problems contribute to continued use they must be the cause of use in the first place. Though this sounds very logical, too much evidence exists that contradicts this assumption. Though it may be true that most addicts cause their own misery by the way they choose to think, this has nothing to do with the cause of addiction. If treatment providers believe that addiction is the result of irresponsible overindulgence; that excessive indulgence leads to addiction; that drugs cause addiction in anyone who overindulges, then this perception will be translated to the client, and this insinuation is likely to hinder their recovery. After all, addicts know far too many people who overindulge and never develop an addiction. This is the social world they live in. In order to believe overindulgence causes addiction in everyone you would have to believe everyone is exactly the same, biologically; that each specific drug has the exact same effect on everyone who uses it, and that all would experience the same repercussions - the same amount of brain damage and neurological adaptation. But this is not the case. Every brain responds and reacts to various drugs differently with some being more severely affected by them than others.

The question is; what is behind these different reactions? Are they a psychological reaction based on one's psychological and emotional well-being or a biological reaction to the drug? The answer is quite simple. Ask anyone who has recovered from alcoholism, given they have gained an adequate degree of psycho-emotional health, if they can now control their use of alcohol on a continual basis. Evidence continues to show that no matter how well a person becomes, they can never regain full control of their use once they have lost it. This is one reason providers teach clients that the only way to overcome addiction is to never use again; addicts will respond to the drug the same way they always have, if not worse, and nearly any degree of using will lead them right back into their addiction. This has been observed over and over again.

Therefore, the cause of addiction is not very likely to be a matter of poor psycho-emotional health, but rather the ignorance of one's own uniquely different biological reaction to the chemical in question. As far as we know, everyone responds to various drugs differently and that biological reactions never improve, they only get worse.

This may explain why only a certain percentage of the population ever becomes addicted, and why others, even most people with psychological problems never do. Viewing addiction from the biological perspective explains *why* it not only attacks the emotionally ill, but the healthy, the rich, the poor, the educated, the uneducated, the famous, etc.

For example, in 2010 I read a peer reviewed journal study in which the research team claimed that one in ten children who smoke just one cigarette, will eventually become addicted to them; that they will have no defense against the addiction because of their genetic predisposition - their biological response to nicotine on the brain. Two independent research teams from different countries, the U.S. and Iceland, both identified the same genetic variant on chromosome 15 to be responsible for this (Researchers, 2010). Also, just a few years ago, researchers identified a transporter gene they believe to be responsible for the drinking intensity apparent in alcoholics; the serotonin transporter gene – SLC6A4. And the 118G variant of the mu-opioid receptor has been, for a while now, suspect to playing an integral part in the increased dopamine reaction observed in alcoholics – please note, not everyone, just alcoholics (Study, 2007).

Apparently, there is no limit to the evidence out there confirming that chemical addictions are beyond mental control for some people, and that's not even mentioning the identical twin studies of some fifty or sixty years ago, which also support it, including more recent ones that confirm the role of genetics in opiate addiction (Opioids, 2012). But again, that is not what this book is about. I have nothing to prove here. The research has already done that. I am just bringing it to your attention.

The point here is, although the evidence is out there, current treatment approaches still view addiction as the result of life experiences and the inability to respond to them in a positive manner; and, it is this perspective that appears to be a great hindrance and barrier to recovery for most addicts.

The way an addict views his or her addiction will have a huge impact on how well they respond to treatment and how long it will take for them to recover, as well as how stable their recovery will be should they obtain it. Therefore, the real question we should be asking ourselves is not what is correct, for we have reasons to support both views of causation; but which perspective will work the best for those in need, to which I believe the answer is more than obvious. We need to do a better job of teaching addicts about their biological condition.

As I have stated, the issue of causation has affected the treatment of mental health patients and those with addictions for centuries, and it will continue to be a part of treatment indefinitely. It cannot be avoided. And, with all the evidence of biological causation mounting up year after year, I cannot help but wonder why the psychosocial perspective of causation continues to prevail in treatment facilities today. Why does the perception of mental failings continue to prevail as the primary cause of addiction in a field that claims not to blame the addict; and, in spite of all the scientific evidence to the contrary? Can it be the result of:

- A misinterpretation of biologic vulnerability? (**dysfunction vs. biological reaction**)
- Personal experience with psychotropic substances? (**biased opinions**)
- Fear of releasing patients from their responsibility? (**best intentions**)

Many well intentioned people get stuck in their own preconceived notions about the cause of addiction. One such man was Richard S. Sander, M.D., a board-certified psychiatrist who wrote a book entitled *Thinking Simply about Addiction: A Handbook for Recovery.*

In the first few pages, Dr. Sander briefly describes some of his own frustrations with treating patients with addictions. He could not understand why so many of his patients would follow his treatment plans explicitly and then relapse shortly after being discharged. It was when his new clinical director, a recovered alcoholic, talked him into attending a few Alcoholic Anonymous (AA) meetings that he began to understand what addiction really was. It was through these meetings, in which he heard hundreds of personal testimonies, that he realized he had not learned much of anything about addiction in all his many years of excellent education. People were getting sober without any professional help what-so-ever and Dr. Sander set out to find the *how* and *why* of it. Eventually he learned that addiction was more than just a lack of constraint, or poor choices. He learned that it stems from a biological reaction to use. "The modern view is that addiction is a disease, <u>a disorder rooted in brain chemistry</u>.... Something no one chooses – a psycho-physiological *reaction* that has a life of its own – an addiction" (Sander, 2009 pp.1-2).

No wonder why so many professionals in the field struggle with the concept of biological vulnerability as being the underlying cause of addiction. Throughout all my years in education, I was amazed to find all the references to addiction as something people did to themselves – if they are not careful. It is this perspective that students are bombarded with for years and years. I cannot count the number of books, from counseling to nursing to anthropology, where I have found references to addiction in this presumptuous and negative light. No wonder so many professionals, from all professions, have such a low opinion of the illness called addiction.

As I have been emphasizing, there are really only two basic approaches to the treatment of chemical addictions and each one of them stems from a *belief* of what really causes addiction. Each of these perspectives, the biological and psychosocial, will affect one's concept of what an addiction is; how it develops; motivational tactics; treatment approaches; what is needed for recovery; what constitutes recovery; the stigma of addiction; and professional conduct.

How can we possibly be very effective at treating addiction if we are unsure of what addiction is, or have a misconception of its root cause? A misconception of what recovery actually is? We must know exactly what addiction is, and be able to convey this knowledge before we can successfully treat it. Simply treating the manifestation of symptoms (i.e., high impulsivity, low self-esteem, attitudes toward use, etc.) without addressing the *how* and *why* of the condition is grossly inadequate, especially with all the evidence we have today. Addressing addiction from the biological perspective clarifies many of these issues. Alcoholics Anonymous has endorsed the use of the biological perspective for over eighty years now, and it has more than proven its effectiveness. If we are earnest about improving treatment, we must take a good honest look at what's been going on and where we can make some changes. But first, we must know exactly what it is we are treating: what exactly is a chemical addiction?

TANGIBLE -
"Capable of being
precisely identified or
realized by the mind"
- Merriam-Webster (2000)

Chapter 4

What is Addiction?

The English word dates back to at least 1599. It comes from the Latin "addictionem," meaning an awarding or a devoting. It has also been used to mean a penchant or a tendency. But the question is, what does it mean to us now? Why is it, within the field of treatment today, we still do not have a universally agreed upon definition for addiction? Can it be that this word, addiction, means one thing to one person and something entirely different to another? Can it be that causational beliefs also affect and impact what we think of as addiction? Or, could it be, that for most people, including professionals in the field, chemical addictions are simply not understood very well?

According to Dr. Nora Volkow from the National Institute on Drug Abuse (NIDA), addiction is, *"A chronic, relapsing brain disease that is characterized by compulsive drug seeking and use, despite harmful consequences. It is considered a brain dis-*

ease because drugs change the brain; they change its structure and how it works. These brain changes can be long lasting and can lead to many harmful, often self-destructive, behaviors" (NIDA, 2010).

The American Society of Addiction Medicine (ASAM) defines addiction as, "*A primary, chronic disease of brain reward, motivation, memory and related circuitry.* Dysfunction in these circuits leads to characteristic biological, psychological, social and spiritual manifestations. This is reflected in an individual pathologically pursuing reward and/or relief by substance use and other behaviors" (ASAM, n.d. - short version).

These definitions acknowledge the biological components of addiction. From them we can ascertain that the toxic effects of drugs on the brain can, and often does, lead to a disease-like condition that helps to explain the destructive behaviors seen in addicts; however, they do little to explain why only some people with a predilection for the use of a specific substance develop an addiction and others do not.

Bear in mind, using the word "disease" is a disputable concept that is not universally accepted. The word disease indicates disorder or dysfunction, but addiction is neither. For example, ingesting toxic substances without falling victim to their effects can be considered normal, as in the case of socially accepted drinking. However, the consumption of toxic substances is not a normal function of the human body just because most people can consume them without causing themselves much harm. Similarly, neither is it a dysfunction or disorder if some people are more affected by a toxic substance than others.

There is also a problem with the wording: "despite harmful consequences." Almost assuredly harmful consequences are occurring deep within the brain of those vulnerable to what psychotropic substances can do to them. In this way, people can still be addicted even if they are lucky enough to escape or avoid what most people would consider to be harmful consequences; such as losing a job, getting into an accident, or the destruction and loss of close relationships.

The problem of defining what an addiction is can be quite a challenge. For example, if a person believes that chemical addictions arise out of psychological reasons for getting high they would probably view chemical addictions more like process addictions. In response, they are likely to come up with definitions that imply alternate causations, such as this one from the American Psychological Association:

"Addiction is a condition in which the body must have a drug to avoid physical and psychological withdrawal symptoms. Addiction's first stage is dependence, during which the search for a drug dominates an individual's life. An addict eventually develops tolerance, which forces the person to consume larger and larger doses of the drug to get the same effect" (American Psychological Association, n.d.).

Or this one, from Psychology Today, which states, *"Addiction is a condition that results when a person ingests a substance (e.g., alcohol, cocaine, nicotine) or engages in an activity (e.g., gambling, sex, shopping) that can be pleasurable but the continued use/ act of which becomes compulsive and interferes with ordinary life responsibilities, such as work, relationships, or health.* Users may not be aware that their behavior is out of control and causing problems for themselves and others" (Psychology Today, n.d.).

Both of these definitions are substantially different from the two cited at the beginning of this chapter, (and the last one makes no distinction between process and chemical addictions, implying that they are basically one and the same). But what is the reason for these substantial differences? The second set of definitions has been influenced by causational beliefs that differ from what our scientific evidence suggests. After all, these last two definitions do not come from a medical or scientific standpoint, but from a purely psychological viewpoint; a view that has dominated and influenced public opinion for centuries. Isn't it time for change? Developing a firm understanding of what a chemical addiction actually is can provide us with a more accurate, precise, and universal definition.

First, from the scientific evidence we now have, we can be pretty confident that all chemical addictions stem from a biopsychosocial *reaction* to a psychotropic substance. Even so, this does not define what a chemical addiction actually is. Below is a definition I believe we can all agree upon, as long as we agree that there would be no such thing as a chemical addiction if it were not for the induction of a specific chemical substance.

A chemical addiction is a *chemically induced mental illness*; such that, in the absence of the chemical, distress ensues; it presents as mild to severe, persistently disruptive thoughts and/or cravings for the effects of a specific substance to squelch or enhance feelings of biological, psychological, or sociological origins, and may include mild to severe cognitive, emotional, and behavioral disturbances.

Put more simply, *addiction is the inability to control one's consumption of a psychoactive substance. It is an abnormally strong or intense desire-to-use a psychoactive substance.* This desire may start out as hardly recognizable at first, but for those vulnerable to addiction, this desire grows and grows (craving) until eventually it consumes the individual's every waking hour. It is a desire that can become so strong that the person is literally robbed of any real choice over whether or not they continue to use. This represents the progression of addiction and this is why addiction is never a choice. Most people can control their desire-to-use a chemical substance, but this is not how it is for an addict. For the addict, this desire-to-use sneaks up on them like a thief in the night. One day they may be thinking that they are still in control, and the next, all bets are off and they are over the edge; they have lost all control over whether or not they use and how much they use when they do. Of course, this does not happen overnight. There has been a lot going on ever since their first use, much of which has to do with the extent of one's individual level of biological vulnerability – what the drug has done to their brain over time with repeated exposure. This does not happen to all people who indulge in the recreational use of a psycho-active (affect) or psycho-tropic (change) substance, nor does every substance impact every user in exactly the same way.

This is why addiction is such an elusively dynamic condition, and identifying it can be can be quite a challenge for both the addicted and the professional, especially in its early stages. One significant identifying feature may be the loss of one's control over one's *amount of use* when they do engage in using. Some people experience this the very first time they try a substance, and for others it may take years, if it progresses to this level at all. Of course, the substance of use will be a big determinant as well. Unless a person receives a pleasurably positive response to a substance, addiction is not even possible. This fact alone indicates all chemical addictions stem from individual biological reactions - a prerequisite one might say. However, it is also very clear that psychological and social conditions play a significant role in whether or not a person with a positive reaction to a chemical substance will actually develop an addiction or not.

The two most salient features of a chemical addiction are: (1) loss-of-control over *quantity* of use (how much they use when they do use); and (2), loss-of-control over *frequency* of use (how often one engages in use); however, these two aspects of loss-of-control are not always discernable. One aspect is due to biological *effects*, and the other is due to biological *adaptation*. Since most, if not all, addicts absolutely love the effects of their substance, or substances, they are very likely to be thinking they are choosing to use, rather than responding to the drug's effects upon them. To understand this, Baudelaire does a remarkable job of describing the loss-of-control (quantity) he observed in Edgar Allen Poe:

> He drank, not as an epicure, but barbarously, with a speed and dispatch altogether American, as if performing a homicidal function, as if he had to kill something inside himself, a worm that would not die. – (as cited in Goodwin, 1988, p. 136)

This is what it is like for the alcoholic. It is a prime example of how the drug (alcohol) can take over the vulnerable person's will. This is the action of alcohol on the brain, which has very little to do with anything else. When this response is present, it is beyond the person's conscious control.

Loss-of-control over *frequency* of use is a little harder to understand because it usually develops over time as the brain adapts to excessive quantities of a drug – when the brain alters its biological components (nerves and receptors) to accommodate the excessive exposure. There are also many psychological and social adaptations that can occur over time with use as well. So, this is where we need to weed out the actual underlying cause. As it is, loss-of-control over *quantity* of use and loss-of-control over *frequency* of use are interconnected and solely dependent upon one's individual degree or level of biological vulnerability – genetic predisposition.

In other words, loss-of-control over quantity of use can lead to a loss-of-control over frequency of use, and loss-of-control over frequency of use can lead to loss-of-control over quantity of use. This is where it gets a little tricky; we need to understand why a person would use a specific substance in the first place, especially if their reaction is that of loss-of-control. Is it because of being socialized to use (as people are supposed to drink), a bad attitude (moral failure), mental deficiencies, or a biological reaction? Well, I think one of our most famed, respected, and adored presidents of all time can shed some light on this (and he wrote this over 150 years ago):

> In my judgment such of us who have never fallen victim [to alcoholism] have been spared

more by the <u>absence of appetite</u> than from any <u>mental or moral superiority</u> over those who have. Indeed, I believe if we take habitual drunkards as a class, their heads and their hearts will bear an advantageous comparison with those of any other class. – Abraham Lincoln (as cited in Goodwin, 1988, p. 27)

This may not be as convincing as the scientific evidence we have today, but it does speak volumes about the actual and obvious cause of addiction. Whether a person's addiction develops from loss-of-control over frequency or quantity, neither can happen without an appetite for the substance. And, this is biologically determined. Remember my reference to the different levels of intensity found only in alcoholics? This evidence tells us that some people are going to like the effects of a substance much more than another person. Even Abraham Lincoln was known to toss back a couple of shots in the evening once in a while, however, he wasn't afflicted with a thirst for it.

A lot more can be said about how the loss-of-control over frequency of use develops, and we will be getting to that in future chapters, but first it is important to understand that addiction is the use of a psychotropic substance that is beyond the person's conscious control. This is how all addictions start and why they are so sneaky. All addicts start out with a predilection for a specific substance and a perceived control over their use, and at some point they are driven to use without their conscious awareness of this change. For the addict, there are underlying forces that drive their behavior to use, and again, this is why addiction is never a choice, nor is using the result of a series of poor choices to use. This is because most people can indulge in drug use rather regularly without ever becoming addicted.

So, addiction is having an uncontrollable desire-to-use a psychotropic substance. The key word here is uncontrollable. Addicts, regardless of which substance they may be addicted to, cannot control their desire-to-use. For the addicted person, this desire-to-use can be overwhelming and seems to appear whenever feelings are aroused, good or bad, excited or bored. For most people, having a desire to use, say having a couple of beers at a party, is no problem. However, this is not the case for those who lose all control of their consumption once they begin. They are having a different reaction (different effects). They can appear to have some control once in a while, but for them this temporal bit of control is just a ruse. For the addicted, anytime they use is like the roll of the dice; they may lose all control of their consumption, or they may not. Even with all the best intentions, once they start using they cannot say with any degree of certainty how much they will have once they start, and this has nothing to do with a lack of will power. I have heard it said, that for the addict, will-power is about as useless as trying to control diarrhea. They cannot will the desire away any more than they can will diarrhea to stop. This is the loss-of-control of addiction. At times, they may be forced to stop using, usually due to external forces, or they may end up on a binge for two or three days. This can happen regardless of any prior commitments made, or just prior to any opportunities they are looking forward to. This is hard for the average person to comprehend, as it goes against all rational thinking, and the addict knows this all too well.

For the addicted, there is an ever present desire-to-use lurking just beneath conscious awareness, standing ready to emerge with an overwhelming force at any given moment, good, bad, or indifferent. Russell Brand, a recovered addict himself, described this ever present desire-to-use perfectly in his touching tribute to Amy Winehouse after her untimely and premature death in 2011 at the age of 27:

> "All addicts, regardless of the substance or their social status share a consistent and obvious symptom; they're not quite present when you talk to them. They communicate to you through a barely discernible but un-ignorable veil. Whether a homeless smack head troubling you for 50 pence for a cup of tea or a coked-up, pinstriped exec foaming off about his 'speedboat,' there is a toxic aura that prevents connection. They have about them the air of elsewhere, that they're looking through you to somewhere else they'd rather be. And of course they are. The priority of any addict is to anesthetize the pain of living to ease the passage of the day with some purchased relief." – Russell Brand (OMG/Yahoo, 2011).

Whether under the influence of a substance or not, this constant desire-to-use is a hallmark of addiction. Sadly, though, addicts do not seem to recognize that they carry this desire-to-use with them until they have recovered and notice that something is missing, something that has been commonly referred to as the "hole in the soul," a feeling of discontent. During their addiction they are rarely, if ever, satisfied where they are at unless they are using. As a result, they become very preoccupied with themselves, and without even realizing it, everything within their world becomes all about themselves. It is kind of like having a paper cut and no matter how much you try to ignore it, your attention always returns to the pain. For the addict, the pain is within the soul.

In addiction, this reaction is likely to be caused by the inability of the neurological system to return to a normal state after use – we have evidence to suggest that some people will return to normal dopamine levels after use and others will not. This reaction intensifies with the progression, and before the addict even realizes it, their whole world revolves around using. Their whole life becomes an endless decision of whether or not to use. Not to use is to suffer, and this is probably why they can endure so much psycho-emotional pain in other areas of their life. After all, they have had years of practice.

An inability to return to a normal baseline of feeling okay without use, along with a constant obsession with self, is probably what leads to all the psychological problems so commonly observed in those with addictions. They start to rationalize about everything that would make them okay. For example, they start to think that they would be okay, happy, satisfied, or fulfilled *if only* this or that happened. This is known as the coping mechanism of rationalizing. This is when they start to blame every problem in their life on others and external situations, which they try to control, but cannot (e.g., *if only* others did this or that; *if only* they had more money; *if only* everybody did what they wanted, which is always the right thing to do according to the addict; *if only* they did not have bad luck, etc.). The frustration this causes them is so tormenting it literally makes it impossible for them to live in the present. Over time, along with this type of distorted thinking that excessive use produces, and which seeps into their times of sober thinking, their minds become fixated on the past and future, thus producing an inability to be fully present. They end up finding themselves always living for tomorrow and for that someday that will never come. For addicts, all this leads to more and more use because that is the only time they can feel okay, which of course, only worsens their biological condition – the inability to return to a normal baseline of emotional satiety.

I think all of us can relate to this type of thinking to some extent or another, but I suspect it is ten times more destructive and progressive for addicts because of their inability to feel peace and contentment without using; something they cannot easily recognize because they have forgotten what it feels like to be okay and at peace. By the time most addicts enter treatment, the feeling of being okay when sober has been lost for many years.

For some addicts this lack of emotional "okay-ness" is likely to stand in the way of gaining true intimacy with others and establishing rewarding relationships. This is what prevents them from developing into a whole, fulfilled, and satisfied person. When confronted, they will deny they have this constant desire-to-use (addiction) because they do not recognize it, nor will they be aware of how disconnected they are from their own feelings. They can still be very emotional at times, especially when under the influence or in the throes of withdrawal; but make no mistake; this is not the same thing as having the ability to be intimate and be in touch with one's feelings when sober. Chances are, these emotional outbursts are chemically induced over-reactions due to biological changes (on the brain's core structures) and distorted thinking, which can also be very emotionally painful. This is likely to be the reason why they suffer from so many of the psychological problems that are associated with addiction, such as the high prevalence of anger, depression, and anxiety. And, for those who do not suffer serious consequences from their addiction, for whatever reasons (e.g., lower levels of biological adaptation, living close to a supply, not driving, etc.), they may live their whole life in such a state; living for 5 pm every day, or for the weekends when they can use more freely without having to be troubled by daily responsibilities.

It may be very likely that the constant desire-to-use is so subtly familiar, that it is not recognized until something stirs the emotions and awakens it from its slumber; like any stressful situation, or the excitement of something enjoyable. It does not have to be something perceived as "bad." This explains why many addicts get intoxicated on some drug, just when something they have been working hard for is about to be achieved. This makes even more sense when we understand the biological adaptations that occur on the emotional regulatory center of the brain (for those who are more vulnerable to biological adaptations). It is well known that drugs highly affect this regulatory structure, which is called the limbic region. It also explains why some drinkers who appear to have a reasonable amount of control over their quantity and frequency of use suddenly lose all control when they experience times of emotional upheaval, never to regain control ever again (e.g., after the death of a loved one, a divorce, battlefield and other various traumas). Please note:

Stressful life events do not cause addiction in anyone; they just send those who are already biologically vulnerable over the edge.

It is rather normal, especially in modern cultures, to turn to the use of a psychotropic substance to cope with trauma. And for most people, this is perfectly safe. However, experiencing a sudden loss of control in quantity or frequency of use after a traumatic experience has more to do with the biological alterations that have occurred in the brain prior to the trauma, than after the trauma. This makes more sense when we understand that some addicts are primed for such a loss-of-control because of all the drugs they used prior to a traumatic experience. The bottom line is, trauma does not cause addiction in people who are not vulnerable to addiction in the first place.

I will be elaborating on trauma and addictions later, but first it is important to grab a firm understanding of what an addiction really is. I know that defining addiction as the inability to control one's desire-to-use a chemical substance may sound a little non-professional, but in all actuality this phenomenon is reflected in a large portion of the Diagnostic and Statistical Manual of Mental Disorders (DSM-5). This is where the desire-to-use is referred to as cravings. One cannot choose not to crave and the addict's desire-to-use is to put an end to the craving. It is their learned and programmed solution. The other three parts of the diagnosis consist of loss-of-control over consumption and changes in tolerance and withdrawal. Therefore, I think it is a fairly accurate description, even though those in treatment may not see it as such. This is because addiction does not reside in the mind (thinking) so much as it does in one's heart and soul (the core structures of the brain). These structures are sometimes referred to as the "old brain," or the instinctual part of the brain. This is the part of the brain where drugs produce the most effect.

Anyone who has experienced or witnessed the utter "soul-wrenching cries of desire" that come from this area of the brain, in horrid withdrawals, can confirm this for you. At this point it has nothing to do with mental abilities. It is way beyond that; it is a biological response having something to do with the emotional regulatory structures of the brain, a reaction germane to those who are vulnerable to a drug's potentially adverse effects. Make no mistake; drugs do not have the same overpowering effects on everyone, like the inability to feel okay without using and changes in tolerance and withdrawal. In fact, many alcoholics report significant periods of time when they could drink all night long and never wake up with a hangover.

Addiction also appears to affect the unconscious core beliefs that are presumed to determine one's personality and drive one's behavior. I have met and known many an addict who has for one reason or another quit using for very long periods of time, usually for being incarcerated as a result of their addiction, only to return to using as soon as they were released. This is because they never learned that it was the drug that caused their addiction in the first place. It does not matter if they have been sober for one, two, five, or ten years. If the addiction (the desire-to-use) has not been addressed, battled, and conquered, it will remain. Many of them, after many years of abstinence are under the illusion that they can now control their use; however, it is almost always external forces that are responsible for this self-deception. This could be the responsibilities of a job, a spouse or girlfriend/boyfriend dragging them home, illnesses, a hangover (with the phenomenon of feeling okay the following day), others cutting them off, putting on a good appearance, running out of money, etc. These are the external factors that make it hard for addicts to identify their addiction within. These periods of abstinence, which can last for months, or even years, can fool them into believing they are still in control of their use; and therefore, not an addict. And, since nobody wants to think of themselves as that vulnerable or weak, they will resist the thought or possibility of having an addiction very strongly. They are very likely to deny that such a condition (addiction) even exists. They will fight off a diagnosis of addiction with all they have and even prefer death, as so many actually do. In a way, I cannot blame them. Let's be honest, who would want to be associated with such a stigmatized and disgraceful condition?

This is why it is so hard to assist addicts. They will continue to get worse and worse, with endless bouts of loss-of-control and humiliation, until they just cannot stand themselves anymore. The problem is, even after they stop using, they still have the desire-to-use. This is when many of them start to admit that there may be something wrong with them; however, without knowing what it is and not wanting to believe that they are mentally ill, or behaving badly, which is what the psychosocial perspective promotes, many of them will continue using with the attitude that they will just have to do the best they can and try to stay out of trouble by planning their use a little better (e.g., living close to where they can get their drug, using at home, not using while driving, etc.). This will only last for so long because the "disease," or more accurately, *condition* of addiction is chronic and progressive if left untreated.

One reason it may be so hard to intervene before an addiction gets so severe is the lack of sufficient answers; meaning answers that addicts can accept. Obviously, being told they are mentally ill, or that they are just behaving badly, is not working for them. This was an insufficient explanation for Bill Wilson and the early alcoholics of AA in the 1930's, and it appears to be just as insufficient today. Somehow, somewhere deep inside, all addicts know there is something more to it. They can feel it. It is the same force that drives people to eat, drink, and breathe. Eventually, the drug takes over.

Like Anne Wilson Schaef stated in her book, *When Society Becomes an Addict*, years ago, one must first accept that they have a problem before it can be addressed (Schaef, 1987). This calls for acceptable answers; an explanation that addicts can identify with and accept; an explanation of what addiction is - what causes it, and how it develops. It really has nothing to do with what you and I think or believe; it is all about what works best for the client. I remember reading a statement by Irvin Yalom in which he makes a comment on what should be considered a valid explanation for any intervention. In it he states that if a person believes God has healed them, *and they are healed*, then this belief is just as much of a valid explanation as any other (Yalom & Leszcz, 2005). As you may recall from the previous chapter, recovery is all about developing some very powerful and rock solid beliefs.

Therefore, addicts must find explanations that they can accept and believe-in before they can begin to recover. In their minds, the problem may just be a lack of control over using, which may be all they want from treatment. Most addicts go through this phase whether they realize it or not because they absolutely love their drug. They are desperately trying to find any way possible to keep on using, but without any consequences; and, they do not recognize this most desperate attempt to keep on using as their addiction. Consequently, all the treatment in the world will not help them if they do not know in their hearts and minds what the real problem is. Some will reach the point where they have lost everything of value to them and still they cannot stop using. This is when they are finally ready to accept treatment at any cost, even if it means being mentally ill. As you may recall, this state of utter despair is known as "hitting bottom." This is when they give up the fight to be "normal."

When they reach this point, the how or why of their addiction is of no concern to them — they are right at the point where most treatment providers want them, at their "bottom," and this is why most treatment providers profess that the cause of addiction is of no concern to them.

As I have previously mentioned, the belief that addicts must hit their bottom before treatment can be effective is likely

to be the result of poor treatment. It is also why the psychosocial perspective appears to work, when in fact, it may only work
for those who have reached such low levels of despair. A despair
that is so great, being mentally ill is no longer a barrier.

It is true that most addicts develop a willingness to engage
in treatment through a long and debilitating decline. Through
all the pain and suffering of their addiction they eventually become willing to accept all the psychosocial explanations given
to them for their condition. I believe we can do much better. It
may actually be the psychosocial perspective of causation which
perpetuates the belief that addicts must hit their "bottom" first.
As it stands, treatment is the last resort for addicts who cannot
envision how they can survive if they keep on using, and they
cannot envision how they can survive if they quit using. This
is known by members of Alcoholic Anonymous as the "jumping off place." At this point they must make a choice; to accept
the confirmation that they are indeed mentally ill and accept
treatment at any cost or they can choose to keep on using, even
if it means certain death. And sadly to say, this happens all too
often. That's if they don't hasten their death by committing
suicide first.

As harmful as the psychosocial perspective appears to be,
a likely reason for its dominance in the field is that the desire-
to-use is always the response to life's situations and challenges,
which are psychosocial issues. However, addicts also get intense
urges of this desire-to-use during various times of the day. For
example, when they are hungry or thirsty (instead of recognizing hunger and thirst), various smells they come across that remind them of their drug, doing something out of habit, feeling

tired, and for the greatest reason of all, which is basically, *not wanting to feel as they do when they are not using.* Over and over again you will hear addicts say they just want to use, but what they are really telling you is that they do not want to feel the way they do, at that particular time. In all actuality, their brain has been programmed to the solution of their problem instead of to the problem itself, which is always, *not wanting to feel the way they do when sober.* This is a most natural psychological response to a biological illness.

For the addict, the psychological "want" to use becomes an automatic response to all of life's ups and downs, and this occurs whether they use or not. And, because there are times when they are unable to use, they fool themselves into thinking they are in control. These are just short periods of suffering for the addict. Addicts, because they always have the desire-to-use locked within, never actually need a reason to use; it's just easier on their own self-image if they have one. Thus, many will unconsciously look for excuses to use, like: getting fired, getting hired, arguing with a spouse, getting a promotion, not getting a promotion, car breaking down, buying a new car, and any or all of life's little ups and downs. This reaction leads to a very detrimental way of thinking. What starts out as an excuse to use gets misinterpreted as an inability to cope with many of life's little challenges, which is only a half-truth. It is true that stress activates cravings (even after months and years of abstinence), which fits nicely into the psychosocial perspective, but this is not why addicts use. They use because they just plain have to use, stress or no stress.

As the progression worsens, the irrational way of thinking

that people experience while under the influence of a psycho-tropic drug starts to take over their thinking while they are *not* under the influence. For example, one may come up with a great way to handle a problem while drunk, and when they wake up the next morning they may say something like, "What on earth was I thinking? That was a crazy idea, I'll never do that." However, after a while, what they would have thought of as crazy in the past no longer seems so crazy. This is when their drug induced irrational thinking starts to take over their sober rational mind. They start to respond to all of life's challenges and experiences, good or bad, as though they were under the influence of a drug. This leads to a whole array of negative coping mechanisms. And, of course, they cannot recognize these changes either. These are only some of the many psychological adaptations that occur with chemical addictions, which is something I will be referring to in Part Two.

Obviously, all the psychosocial issues that contribute so heavily to use must be addressed in treatment; however, all too often these issues are thought of as causal features instead of consequences. And, this can hinder the likelihood that those caught in addiction will accept their condition. Addressing the many psychosocial issues that addicts experience is not treating the addiction. What it does do is provide clients with the strength and courage to fight the battle of addiction within; to fight off the desire-to-use, which are one and the same. However, they must be told about this battle that only they can fight; the battle between the mind's rational thinking (in the prefrontal cortex) and the desire-to-use; the addiction, which resides in the heart and soul, in the core structures of the brain (i.e., the nucleus acumens NAc, amygdala, hippocampus, thalamus, and the ventral tegmental area VTA, all of which are associated with motivation and pleasure in the mesolimbic region). These are not thinking structures, such as in the cortex, they are the ones much deeper, the ones responsible for urges and cravings. Urges are *waves of intense unease*, whereas, cravings are a less intense but more steady feeling of unease, a *constant gnawing*.

A biological reaction may cause addiction (not feeling okay without using), but addiction also includes a relationship that is built up over many years between the user and the drug. This relationship is so strong it usually takes precedence over any other human relationship. It also explains why those who maintain sobriety for years and years, such as being incarcerated, return to their drug of use when they are released. This only makes sense; nothing on God's green earth can do for them what their drug can, and more importantly, it never lets them down. Unless one's love for the drug is acknowledged and broken, like a bad relationship, it will remain.

This battle, the one that only the addict can fight, is the battle between "I want to use so very badly" (very deep emotional longings) and the voice that says "I should not use" (in the mind). The mind is the common sense that says using hurts me; it causes me so much trouble, and yet I still continue to use; therefore, I must be as insane as I have been lead to believe. Yes, most treatment providers do a lot of insinuating if they are coming from the psychosocial perspective. They tend to attribute addiction to the distress of various life-course hardships. This can appear to be very logical, empathetic, and helpful; however, it actually works against recovery in two significant ways:

The psychosocial perspective lacks the ability to identify and address the actual addiction.

Again, addressing the many psychological issues associated with addiction does nothing for the addiction itself. Low self-esteem, depression, anxieties, fears, etc., are not, and I repeat, are not, addiction. They are not even addiction when you put them all together. They are exactly what they are, psychological problems and nothing more. Many people who do not have an addiction have these same psychological problems. Likewise, addressing social-environment problems does nothing for the addiction either. They help in the same way; to protect the client from further harm and provide strength for the battle, but they offer no help in *identifying* what addiction is or *addressing* (treating) the actual cause – the core-driven unease that addicts live with when they are sober.

Any insinuations that psychosocial issues are the reason or cause of addiction only serve to divert the addict's attention away from their problem, the actual addiction. And, they can have very negative effects. First, they imply the person is mentally incapable of handling life without using, which has sent many an addict flying right out the door. Secondly, they increase anger and stress by allowing the addict to put the blame for their addiction on themselves, others, and/or their life's circumstances. This is a common practice today, and it is very dangerous and self-defeating because, as we all know, anger and stress are the number one causes of relapse. Why would we want to encourage such thinking?

The evidence we have strongly suggests that neurological adaptations, along with a significant decline in the brain's normal neurotransmitter levels is what is responsible for the urges and cravings addicts' experience. It also explains why addicts feel less-than okay when sober, prompting them to keep on using. In addicts, unlike most people, the brain does not return to normal neurological functioning after use. The alterations are long-lasting. This is why addicts have a constant feeling of unease when they are sober for any length of time, and why they have a strong desire-to-use in response to all of life's emotional arousals, big or small (e.g., distress, boredom, stress, excitement). As addicts continue in their use, they start to feel increasingly less-than okay when not using.

In recent animal experiments researchers have confirmed that some animals do, in fact, return to normal dopamine baselines faster than others. These experiments also found that some may never return to normal baselines after addiction (Kuhar, 2012). This supports the argument that some people are more impacted by drugs than others, and that biological adaptation is very likely to be responsible for chemical addictions, the desire-to-use that underlies all our psychosocial explanations for using. Since we now know that the emotional pleasure center of the brain is affected by various chemicals, it only stands to reason that this is the part of the brain (the mesolimbic region) that would be the area most affected. Some people experience urges and cravings long after they stop using and this phenomenon is most likely due to changes in the person's neurotransmitter baseline, specifically the depletion of dopamine, serotonin, and other neurotransmitters.

NEUROTRANSMITTER BASELINE

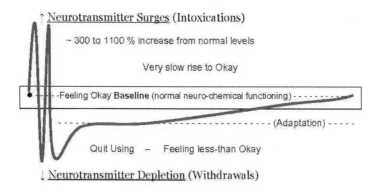

↑ <u>Neurotransmitter Surges</u> (Intoxications)

~ 300 to 1100 % increase from normal levels

Very slow rise to Okay

--Feeling Okay **Baseline** (normal neuro-chemical functioning) - - - - - - - -

- (Adaptation) - - - - -

Quit Using — Feeling less-than Okay

↓ <u>Neurotransmitter Depletion</u> (Withdrawals)

This diagram shows how the repeated use of psychotropic substances can interfere with normal neurochemical functioning. When the brain doesn't have any use for more neurotransmitters when high, like dopamine or serotonin for instance, it slows the production of them. Also, in the regulation of neurotransmitter levels, the brain's neuronal re-uptake and receptor sites appear to die off when neurotransmitter levels are consistently too high. There is also evidence of whole neurons dying off. These are actual physical alterations to one's brain structures from use, which is probably the body's natural response to drugs in an attempt to regain normalcy, a process known as homeostasis. When it comes to chemical addictions, these biological adaptations can no longer be ignored.

Now that we know what chemicals can do to the brain, it is easy to see how the three biopsychosocial factors of addiction incite and contribute to use. This would lead many of us to believe that each of these factors work in conjunction with each other to "cause" addiction. However, this may not be the case at all. Of these three factors, evidence suggests that one of these factors must be present first - biological vulnerability.

When we view the biopsychosocial factors of addiction as symptoms (the changes we can see and measure), we can gain an even greater understanding of the totality of addiction. Like cancer, we don't really know where it stems from, but we do know that both addiction and cancer are chronically progressive conditions. Take a cancerous tumor for example. With the tumor being the primary symptom of cancer (observable) we can easily understand that the tumor did not cause itself to form, something else did. However, if we were to watch the tumor grow, spread, and take over other organs of the body, we may easily conclude the tumor to be cancer, but it is actually the primary symptom of cancer. Likewise, the primary symptom of addiction, the use (observable), also grows, spreads, and appears to cause more use. The point here is that symptoms, which are visible, like the tumor, do not actually cause addiction.

Watching an addict continue to use despite consequences is only another symptom of addiction. The addiction lies much deeper. The cause of addiction, much like the cause of cancer, is something unseen. However, evidence continues to suggest that addiction is most likely due to different neurological reactions, which include both effects and adaptations. It cannot be controlled by mere will-power or even superior psychological health. It can however, be halted and arrested early on through identification, acceptance, and conscious effort.

Clearly, the desire-to-use is a most powerful force; a force so strong that it overrides basic human needs, such as hunger and thirst. This is not psychological. One cannot think themselves into being hungry or thirsty, nor can we ignore those urges for very long when we get them. Since we know these callings come from physical structures of the brain, it only makes sense that much of an addicts' desire-to-use stems from this uncontrollable source, and probably remains there in much lower degrees of intensity long after cessation of use.

Take skin cancer, for example. We know that excessive exposure to the sun causes skin cancer in some people, but it does not cause skin cancer in everyone who is exposed to the same amount of sun rays. This is because of genetic predisposition. Some people are just more susceptible or vulnerable to the effects of the sun than others; this is a fact. Therefore, we cannot state for a fact that excessive exposure to the sun causes skin cancer in everyone. Likewise, we cannot state for a fact that everyone exposed to the same amount of alcohol, for example, will acquire alcoholism. This is because of genetic predisposition. We know that when kids start drinking at an early age, when the brain is still in its developmental stage, their risk of becoming addicted later in life is increased. Likewise, we also know that when kids start tanning at an early age their risk of developing skin cancer later in life increases. For this reason *all* kids should not use drugs or expose themselves too heavily to the sun. Right? Well, not necessarily. Not every kid who starts drinking or tanning at an early age will ever develop skin cancer, or alcoholism, unless they are biologically prone to these conditions; they *must* be genetically vulnerable to such a *degree* that allows these conditions to develop. We do not all share the same degree of biological vulnerability to the *effects* of the sun on the skin, nor to the *effects* of psychotropic drugs on the brain.

While I am on this sensitive subject, we all know that the human brain is not fully developed until about the age of 21 to 24, so it only makes sense that using at such an early age would "cause" addiction. However, this may not be the case at all since the frontal lobe of the brain is the last to develop. This is the part of the brain responsible for decision-making, impulse control, and processing emotions, all of which are needed to control the use of a psychotropic substance. However, most children who try a psychotropic substance at this early age do not continue to use on a regular basis, nor do they ever develop an addiction. It is, however, the kids who are highly impacted by a substance that do continue to use on a regular basis – the ones who are biologically vulnerable right from the get go; the ones who are genetically predisposed.

So, what's the point? The point is that we may be looking at this young age of use "risk factor" all wrong. It is a fact that using at a young age causes frontal lobe development to be smaller (less mass). I do not dispute this fact at all. However, to go and assume that using at a young age "causes" addiction, is just that; only an assumption. A more accurate way to view this fact, is to understand that only those kids who have an addictive genetic predisposition (GP) to a substance (at the brain's core) are likely to be the only ones using on a continuous basis; thus, this is what accounts for the lower amount of frontal lobe development we see in adult addicts who started using at an early age. These are the people who are going to have this symptom because they are very likely to have been biologically vulnerable right from the get go.

In other words, biologically vulnerable children who started using at an early age are going to do more damage to their brain and have less ability to fight off their addiction, than biologically vulnerable children who started using in adulthood.

This is why we need to inform our children of this danger. We need to inform them of the reality of GP - because these are the kids who are going to suffer from this brain impairment, not the kids without a genetic predisposition.

When we recognize the totality of addiction as involving all three of the biological, psychological, and social-environmental components, *the driving forces behind using*, we can gain an even greater insight into what addiction really is; and thereby, begin to understand that it can be totally eradicated.

Genetic predisposition; which, like the fruit fly experiment I will be presenting later, is partially hereditary. It will be passed down randomly through generations to some people but not to all. However, just because the biological response is permanent, this does not mean the desire-to-use (the addiction) is permanent. As long as one remains sober, and receives treatment for their psychological and social adaptations, one can obtain total freedom from their addiction. This is why the biological aspects of causation are so very important to understand. It can change how we view recovery, and more importantly, sets a real and measurable goal for addicts; which is to be released from their desire-to-use.

What is vitally important to understand here is that addicts must be made aware of this option of complete recovery. This is what will keep them on the path of recovery through the rough times, through of all the psycho-emotional repair and healing. It is the misconception of what addiction is and where it stems from that accounts for the widespread belief that addiction is permanent, and as such, must be addressed indefinitely. Unless addicts know they can recover, and what it means to be fully recovered, they probably never will.

All in all, addiction is a chemically induced mental illness and behavioral health problem that can be overcome through abstinence and treatment. Abstinence alone is insufficient. One must seek to eradicate the desire-to-use, the addiction. Measuring abstinence is not a measure of recovery and only the addict can know how severe or mild their addiction is. They are the ones we have to ask. We also need to know what to ask: How many times did you think of using today? How strong were your urges to use? Are they becoming more intense or more bearable as time goes by? In other words, the measuring of thoughts and urges are a much more accurate and applicable measurement of addiction than mere abstinence.

In brief, the cause of addiction is the drug. Then there are adaptations to the effects of the drug on the brain, which consist of biological, psychological, and social-environmental changes. These are the adaptations that produce the total desire-to-use, which is the addiction. They are the biopsychosocial cravings and they are the driving force behind use. In essence, these forces are the addiction; all three categories of them. These driving forces can be innumerable and consist of things like using attitudes, avoidance of feelings, fears of judgment or rejection, stressful situations, etc. There may be multiple mental health problems involved as well; however, do not confuse mental health problems (e.g., low self-esteem, depression, anxiety, low self-efficacy, etc.) with addiction – the desire-to-use. They may fuel the addiction, but they are independent conditions that need to be addressed separately. This is where addicts build the inner strength to fight off their urges, cravings and obsessions, which is much more than just biological.

It is important to realize addiction is not a choice. When there is a driving force behind use, the choice of whether or not to use is severely compromised. An addict's choice to use is no different than your or my choice to eat or drink; sooner or later we have to give in. This is what it is like for the addict.

The good news is that recovery is a choice; a choice that may need to be made hundreds, if not thousands, of times before the addiction is completely eradicated. Psychosocial issues fuel use, which in turn create more adaptations to the brain, which in turn, create more psychosocial problems, and round and round it goes. This is the progression of the condition.

As I have previously stated, I realize referring to addiction as the desire-to-use might appear too vague and elementary for some. It may even sound a bit ridiculous; however, I have good reason for using this terminology. In all actuality, the desire-to-use, whether mild yearnings or those hard core gut-wrenching feelings that compels addicts to continue in their use, does not present in terms of logical thinking. For example, when addicts are in the grip of strong urges and cravings, their minds do not tell them that there is something wrong and that they need to find out what the problem is; NO, it just tells them "I want to use." It bypasses any thought of *why* and goes directly to the addict's programmed solution, which is to get the drug. (There are biological reasons for why this phenomenon happens, which have to do with the shutting down of specific neurons to the frontal lobe when cravings get intense, but this may be too complicated to get into here.) In any case, this is why the mind does not say, I do not want to feel this way, as what would naturally occur in any non-addicted person. All the addict is aware of is that they want-to-use. So, this is the problem. This is the addiction.

People in early recovery have a very hard time recognizing their addiction when all they can think about is getting their drug and the relief they know is sure to follow. To help them make this connection between "I want to use" (their automatic solution) and the discontent they are feeling without using, calling addiction the desire-to-use makes it a lot easier for addicts to recognize; and thus, provides them with a tangible reality to fight. After all, they surely know what it is to have constant yearnings and thoughts about using, i.e., the desire.

The main point here is just this: with the use of this terminology, in defining addiction as the desire-to-use, addicts not only learn what it is they need to fight – their solution, but they are equipped with how to go about it. They no longer have to fight with making *a decision* on whether or not to use each and every time they get an urge, they have to *not use* in the face of these urges, to fight off their desire-to-use. This is how they can begin to recognize that using is not their problem, but only their solution to their real problem, which is the inability to feel okay without using. This is the empowerment that has been missing for far too long. It is only through acknowledging and surrendering to the craving, and all the other psychosocial forces behind using, that one can begin to fight off their addiction.

Therefore, a chemical addiction is a chemically induced mental illness. It is a mental illness because it is a psychological distress that resides in the mind: where the illness is the longing for the effects of a chemical substance (desire-to-use) – to avert the internal suffering (not feeling okay). It is chemically induced because this desire-to-use reaction is caused by the effects of chemical substances on the brains of those who are susceptible to this reaction (alterations to brain chemistry). For, without the induction of a chemical substance addiction is not even possible.

A chemical addiction presents as an immensely strong desire-to-use and all that this term implies; it includes all the biopsychosocial adaptations that fuel continued use; such as: the biological urges; anhedonia (inability to feel pleasure in everyday activities without use); use as a coping mechanism (stress reliever); intrusive thoughts of using; and one's self-concept as a user; including, the very strong love-like relationship that develops between the user and drug over time.

The degree of comfort and relief that addicts receive from their drug may be such that only they may know the true meaning of what it is like to be addicted; and, the tendency to compare one's personal experience with the use of a drug to another's may be a trap that is best avoided.

In summation, addiction is simply the inability to control one's frequency or amount of a psychotropic substance, regardless of any observable consequences. The real consequences are the ones that cannot be seen. The changes that occur deep within the brain; in the soul, mind, and body – (emotion, thought, and structure). What starts out as a predilection for the effects of a substance (for those who are genetically predisposed to these effects and biological adaptations), eventually turns into a need that is driven not only by biological forces, but the effects of these changes in psychological and sociological adaptations as well; which are extremely hard, if not outright impossible, to recognize, arrest, treat, and conquer on one's own. People with addictions need to seek professional help. Regardless of causal beliefs, professionals possess the knowledge, tools, and skills needed to combat this insidious and deadly illness. And, with the acceptance and proper application of genetic predisposition, they are likely to become much more effective.

DEVELOP -
"To expand by a
process of growth"
- Merriam-Webster (2000)

Chapter 5

Development

Now that we know what an addiction is, it's time to take a look at how and why a person becomes addicted. Obviously, this does not occur overnight. No one tries a substance once, and is instantly addicted right from the get go. It takes a period of using over time in which a person *develops* an addiction. And, as we have learned, the seed of addiction has to be planted into fertile ground – the biological conditions that allow addiction to ocurr.

In this chapter we are going to examine how chemical addictions grow; how they develop and get stronger and more severe over the course of time. To start, we need to know about the fertile ground, the two aspects of biological vulnerability that are involved in the development of chemical addictions.

The biological aspects of addiction involve much more than just the neurological changes and damage drugs can do to the brain. They involve both the varying degrees of <u>effects</u> (intensity of euphoria and degrees of loss-of-control) and the varying degrees of <u>adaptation</u> (neurological changes in tolerance, physical urges and cravings, and anhedonia). For those who develop addictions, both of these aspects of bio-vulnerability are likely to be present. Having one aspect without the other, such as an intensely euphoric reaction to a substance without a low resistance to neurological adaptation, is unlikely to result in addiction. As the evidence suggests, some people are much more resistant to biological adaptations than others. So, even if a person has a highly euphoric reaction to a substance, but they also have a high resistance to neurological adaptation, they are unlikely to develop an addiction. Therefore, both of these biological aspects of vulnerability must be present (high euphoria and low resistance to bio-adaptation).

The concept of losing the mental ability to control the use of a psychotropic substance is sometimes attributed to the abuse of drugs, which makes perfectly good sense; however, this concept does not hold true for those who experience extreme euphoria and loss of control with first use, nor does it explain why so many people can abuse various substances and never become addicted. Obviously there is more to this.

We do know that biological vulnerability can only be treated with abstinence, just like any other biological reaction. This is because, as far as we know, biological reactions rarely change. We also know that psychological and emotional health does improve, but not to such a degree that it can override one's biological response to a psychotropic substance, particularly in those who have developed an addiction. Since I have heard hundreds and hundreds of testimonies describing various developments of addiction, *a complete understanding of addiction must encompass and account for all these variations.* Through my years of study, I have only found one concept capable of this - biological vulnerability. The amount of scientific evidence available to us today is just too enormous to ignore, and all the genetic research and experiments on animals point to biological factors as the only *foundational cause* of addiction. And, since we know that social and psychological factors cannot cause addiction without a positive biological response that encourages use, this evidence suggests that addiction can only stem from biological factors. If this is so readily apparent and obvious, why is this information basically ignored and/or misapplied in treatment?

It would be nice if these few simple facts ended the dispute, but I know how hard it is for some of us to challenge our own long-held beliefs and convictions. I too, once believed that addiction was the result of one's own doing, but after years of studying addiction and carefully examining the evidence, I have gained a much more inclusive view of the illness. First, I know of no one who used a substance once and became instantly addicted. Not that this cannot happen, just that I have never been able to recognize it that early. I have, however, seen very different initial effects from the use of various psychotropic drugs. This would be the variation in *effects* that different people experience. For those who experience extreme degrees of euphoria and pleasure from use, regardless of their life's experiences (and this is very important point), they will inevitably use them again. This is not addiction, this is only natural; a positive attitude toward use has been established. Those at the opposite end of the scale who experience negative effects from use tend to adopt a more negative attitude towards using, and therefore are basically incapable of becoming addicted. And, this is only normal for them as well. It is normal for people to seek pleasure and avoid discomfort – positive and negative reinforcement. Since we know that all drugs affect people differently, seeing various degrees of pleasure along a continuum is only obvious. Therefore, the degree of pleasurable effects from a drug plays an important role in the development of addiction. This is the *effects* part of biological vulnerability. It is the primary reason one uses in the first place, and there is nothing abnormal about this – *when use is controlled*. However, in those who become addicted to various substances, it appears that the intensity of these effects, which includes one's *degree* of euphoria and *degree* of loss-of-control, appear to be extreme.

Many agree that an intense response to a substance may be an early warning sign of addiction. Many addicts have very vivid memories of their first use. They have an uncanny ability to describe every minute detail of their first use with profound awareness. They know exactly where they were at the time of their first use and with whom they used the drug. They can describe how it made them feel and provide very specific details about their first experience, like noticing dew drops glistening off the long blades of grass in the bright afternoon rays of the sun. They can recall everything that was going on in their mind as if it were yesterday. They have an experience so profound they are unlikely to ever forget it. This does not seem to occur with most people, or in those with lower degrees of addiction. Also, it has recently been found that certain areas of the brain in alcoholics are actually stimulated by alcohol rather than producing a more sedating effect, which is what normally occurs in most people. These differences cannot be ignored when considering causation. They are clear indications that something different is going on within the brain. These different reactions suggest that the drug may be initiating neurological changes long before they can be recognized. Addiction does not occur overnight; it takes a period of using, so it only makes sense that those who are more impacted by a substance would develop an addiction much faster than those who are less affected.

Now, as one continues along their natural path of use, which is dependent upon the intensity of the biological *effects* from the drug, the degree of pleasure received from use will correlate with the amount of use one seeks out. This does not mean that once a person receives a great amount of pleasure from use they immediately discard other pleasures in life. This usually develops over time as the brain *adapts*, and of course, the various psychotropic substances being consumed will affect how long this might take. Stronger drugs would take less time than weaker acting drugs, but we also have to take into consideration other independent factors, such as genetically unique degrees of biological resistance to change. One person's brain is going to be more resistant to the neurological changes drugs can cause than another's. This is the biological *adaptation* part of addiction that everyone is so familiar with, as it includes the development of tolerance and withdrawal; however, it is also responsible for the cravings those with addictions experience, and might very well be responsible for psychological and social adaptations *to use* as well.

As people continue along their path of using, they will usually combine their use with other acts of pleasure, such as bowling, golfing, socializing, etc. This is perfectly normal for those who can still find pleasure in other activities without using; however, not all people are affected in the same way. For those more vulnerable to neurological adaptations, the pleasure center of the brain is affected and they become less and less able to experience pleasure in normal activities without using. In other words, other pleasures in life become less and less enjoyable, due to changes in the brain (anhedonia), and they begin to take a backseat to the new pleasure addicts have found in their drug. This is why the development of addiction is so sneaky; this subtle and slow loss of pleasure in normally pleasurable activities goes unnoticed by the addict.

So, in addition to the different effects people experience, some people are more biologically vulnerable to the neurological *adaptations* drugs can cause. Addicts experience biological adaptations of neurological structures in the brain, and again, this is not all one side or the other. There is a continuum of varying degrees of biological vulnerability (resistance to change) among users. Yes, quantity and frequency of use play an important role in this adaptation, but we also have to take into consideration individual protective factors. These include different degrees of resistance to change, not only to biological adaptation, but to psychological and social-environmental developmental factors as well, and psychosocial adaptations from use, which will be addressed in Part Two. This is what accounts for the totality of varying degrees and depths of chemical addictions, the two biological aspects along with the psychosocial adaptations that occur with use. Addiction is not merely having one or not, it involves the degree or depth of the addiction as well; and this varies among those afflicted.

As for the evidence of different biological *effects*, we know that chemicals affect everyone differently, from minor to extreme effects. This is why prescription drugs are always started at the lowest effective dose known, and slowly increased to an effective therapeutic dose on an individual basis. It is also why some people cannot take various medications. When it comes to prescription drugs, individualized reactions (varying degrees of effect) are not even a question. All drugs have a desired effect that is common for the drug being prescribed; however, some people reach the desired or intended effect of a drug at a much lower dosage than what it might take for another person; and, there are always side effects to take into consideration, which are dependent upon the dose administered and the individual's biological response. This is nothing new, we have known of these differences ever since the beginning of medications; however, in applying these known facts to the use of recreational drugs, drugs of pleasure, this knowledge appears to have fallen off the face of the earth. This is proof that drugs impact everyone a little differently, and yet, this knowledge in not even mentioned in the treatment of addictions. Why?

Now, there may be some purely innocent reasons for the suppression of this information, but we can only speculate. It seems to me that any *facts* we have about drugs and how they affect the human body would be very pertinent to the treatment of addictions, especially to those who are so familiar with them. Therefore, it makes one wonder. Why is it that something so readily accepted in the field of medicine would be so readily ignored in the field of chemical addictions? Could it be that it interferes with the *belief* that since most people can control their use, all people should be able to; and, if they can't, well, there must be something seriously wrong with them; something wrong with their mind, character, attitude, etc. Sound familiar? This is the assumption that appears when biological factors are left out of explanations for the *development* of chemical addictions.

It is clearly documented that not everyone receives the same desired effects from use, nor is everyone subject to the same side, adverse, or idiosyncratic effects. For example, alcohol depresses the central nervous system (CNS), cocaine stimulates the CNS, LSD produces hallucinations. These effects, like medications, are the intended or expected effects; however, like medications, they do not produce the same intensity of effect in everyone, nor do all people suffer from the same side or adverse effects. Tolerance excluded, one person may drink six beers, lose all self-control, and suffer a tremendous hangover the next day, while another may not even be fazed by drinking six beers. These are very important aspects to consider in the development of addictions. However, I have never witnessed the use of different biological *effects* being explained as a potential cause of addiction. The only reasonable explanation I can come up with for this is that it does not fit very well into the *belief* of personal responsibility, self-causation.

On the flip side, neurological *adaptation* (brain damage), does fit rather nicely into the *belief* of self-causation, and rather well at that. Because of this, it is often used to show addicts what can happen with the excessive use of drugs. However, the use of this information also shows them what they may have done to themselves, and are continuing to do to themselves if they do not stop using. I have seen this side of biological evidence being used as a therapeutic intervention countless times, but I have to wonder, why is it that only one side of our biological evidence is being used? Could it be to discourage the continued use of a drug, and have nothing to do with causation? Or, is it being used to explain why addicts can never recover? These are questions we need to ask ourselves. Personally, I have heard many an addict tell me that they know they overdid their use of alcohol and drugs and that this is why they can never use again – that they have pickled their brain and a pickle can never go back to being a cucumber. This, I am embarrassed to say, is the only thing addicts are learning from our biological evidence. And, we have so much more to offer.

Let's consider the misuse of our biological evidence in treatment. Despite the extensive knowledge we have about drugs affecting people differently, by producing different degrees of *effects* in people (pharmaceutical), I have only witnessed the use of *adaptation* (damage) being applied in treatment. It is almost as though this selective use of information has been used in this way on purpose, and probably to convict addicts of what they have apparently done to themselves. Some treatment professionals may even believe that adaptations are the only applicable part of our biological evidence. Apparently, it can be very easy for some people to stray away from evidence that contradicts their own well-established beliefs, especially if it means going against the well-established norms of the profession.

This is why our biological evidence is so vitally important, and why we must re-examine how it is currently being applied, so that we may apply it more thoroughly and effectively in the future. It is common knowledge that biological evidence has been used to shame or guilt addicts into recovery. All too often I have heard ex-addicts state this as their reason for why they could no longer use like normal people; that it was because of their own willful and reckless use of their drug; and, that because they have abused this privilege to use, they must now pay the price. How sad is that? Intended or not, they are learning to accept the shame and guilt for what they have apparently done to themselves. These individuals were taught that they caused their own addiction.

This is a problem. People do not consciously and willingly lead themselves down the road to addiction, but instead, are lead down the road by multiple biopsychosocial factors; most likely stemming from their own unique biological reaction to a drug in the first place. I realize this may be hard for many to fully comprehend, but there is an obligation here. We can no longer provide patients with half the truth, half the story. We must provide them with all the evidence if we are going to use any of it at all. And, we must stop putting our own spin on it. Meaning, we must stop implying what we think the evidence means or what we think the evidence is telling us. For instance, if we only show addicts pictures of damaged brains caused by the use of various drugs, are we not accusing addicts and convicting them of their own apparent guilt?

Presenting patients with evidence of biological adaptation (damage), which has been very well documented, has been used for decades to inform patients of the damage drugs can cause. It has not necessarily been used to explain causality, or the fact that those whose brains' adapt to a drug's impact upon them are probably more vulnerable to the effects of the drug than others. This is important to understand.

Biological evidence does not equate to bio-vulnerability unless it is used for this causal purpose and presented as such – evidence to the fact that some people are more vulnerable to neurological adaptation than others.

I suspect we can all think of someone we know that may have drunk very heavily most of their life and never developed alcoholism, or at least, the life-consuming alcoholism that destroys peoples' lives. This is most likely due to a variety of bio-psychosocial factors, but it may also be that these people are more biologically resistance to what drugs can do, especially since we know that it is the amount of consumption, in relation to one's degree of resistance to change, that actually causes addiction. Again, if we are going to present one side of the story, we must also present the other side.

When addicts are presented with gruesome pictures of how devastating drugs can be they respond like most people would - it could never happen to them. This is because, not only is this a rather common human reaction, but as I have previously mentioned, they still believe they have some control over whether or not they use. This kind of evidence cannot be used as a means of motivation, plain and simple.

Merely presenting biological evidence of *damaged* brains has very little, if any, therapeutic effect. However, using both biological *effects* and *adaptations* in explaining the probable *cau-*

sation of their addiction can have an enormous therapeutic effect. See the difference? This is information they need to know and we can use it to provide them with an explanation for why they used like they did in the first place – informing them of how their own uniquely individual biological reaction could have played a major role in the development of their addiction. In this way we can release addicts from all the guilt and shame associated with chemical addictions. It may be helpful to ask ourselves, if addicts are truly unaware of the alterations occurring deep within their brain, is there really any feasible way they could have avoided their addiction? To better understand the process of this biological adaptation, I think this simple diagram can explain it much better than words.

BIOLOGICAL DEVELOPMENT

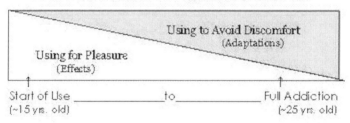

What starts out as using for fun and pleasure slowly changes to using to avoid discomfort (psychological as well as physical) as the brain adapts to the effects of the drug. This is why the development of addiction is so sneaky; and why, by the time the addicted person realizes they are addicted, it is too late – too late to "put the brakes on" their use.

Therefore, when evidence of damaged brains is presented, as it should be, it should be accompanied by the fact that not all people are affected in such drastic ways; that the amount of neurological alteration one can experience from the use of a drug is not only dependent upon the amount of one's consumption, but also, by the amount of one's resistance to biological adaptation, degrees of biologic vulnerability. For example, we know that a Blood Alcohol Concentration (BAC) of 0.70 will kill any human being; however, we do not know how much damage or adaptation one might incur, if any, from an exposure to an alcohol concentration of say, 0.30 or 0.10. One person may be permanently and drastically affected, whereas another person may not be affected at all. These are the unseen human differences we must acknowledge. We cannot continue to assume that everyone would be affected by the same substances, or the amounts of the same substance, in exactly the same way.

The concept of biological vulnerability can be very effective and useful because it rings true with the addict's experience; it helps to explain so many unanswered questions; it explains to the addict why they used like they did and relieves tons of guilt and shame in the process. It allows addicts to forgive themselves and puts the focus of their attention on recovering. The benefits go on and on. And, despite all the benefits that biological vulnerability has to offer, the biased view of self-causation still prevails. So, where does this insistence on personal causation stem from? As I touched upon earlier, one explanation may be that it stems from the counselor's own experience with a psychotropic substance. I have heard several professionals in the field state that they themselves could have been an addict had they not had the good sense to put a limit on their use. This sounds great, and it would hold true if everyone reacted to chemicals substances in exactly the same way. I suspect it is an assumption that helps most people feel good about themselves. This assumption of identical biological reaction contradicts what we know to be true about vulnerability – the different *effects* and *adaptations* people experience from the same substances. Some people are just more biologically susceptible to the effects and adaptations of certain substances than others. This is a fact, not a theory. It is true that poor emotional and psychological health leads to more use, so from a logical perspective, it would appear to be the main or underlying cause of addiction; however, addiction may start long before all the biopsychosocial adaptations set in. It may start with the initiation of use for those who receive very intense *effects*.

I would like to tell you about a patient I once received on intake at a hospital where I worked. This man played a crucial role in the development of my own understanding of biological causation. He had no prior history of addiction and had been an addictions counselor for the past ten years when he came into treatment and I performed his psychosocial assessment. Wow! I was shocked. I had to ask myself, "How could this have possibly happened to a well-seasoned professional?" For one, I can tell you he was like most of us, totally clueless of where addictions really stem from. It snuck up on him like it does everyone else who partakes in the recreational use of a psychotropic substance; and, more importantly, *who is unsuspecting of genetic predisposition.* He, being an addictions counselor himself for a very long time, had believed he possessed some sort of psycho-immunity. He, like so many others in the field, had fallen into the trap of believing addiction was the result of poor choices and psychological deficiencies. As he enjoyed the occasional use of his drug, he was totally unaware of the impact this drug was having on his brain. It was obvious that he had shared the same perspective of so many other well-meaning professionals, people, and addicts alike. Nobody likes to think of themselves as vulnerable to addiction, and without the knowledge of one's own uniquely different level of biological-vulnerability, no one is really safe - except those who do not use any psychotropic substances at all. For in reality, to use a psychotropic substance, without the knowledge of your own bio-vulnerability, is like playing Russian roulette.

This is why it's so important to understand where addictions stem from, so that those who are more vulnerable can be made aware of these differences, and therefore learn to accept their condition more readily than they would if the concept of addiction remains as a mental inferiority or just plain "bad" behavior. As I mentioned in the first few pages, people must know they have a condition, whether it be cancer, hypertension, heart disease, or the like in order to do something about it. The problem with chemical addictions is that no one really knows how vulnerable they are to addiction until it's too late. However, the acceptance of biological vulnerability affords each potential addict the chance of spotting their addictive condition much sooner than they would without it. It gives them the chance to avoid full blown addiction; which, as you will see in the next few pages, is very possible. However, without accepting biological vulnerability, it will continue to be extremely hard for people to accept such a stigmatized and embarrassing condition.

Now, let's try to think out of the box for a second. Let's say that heroin was the accepted recreational substance of use in the U.S. instead of alcohol. We know that heroin is much stronger than alcohol in both effect, and adaptation. And, regardless of varying statistics, we know that about two-thirds of the people who try heroin "for recreational purposes" become addicted and the other third do not. So, from these statistics we can conclude that the one-third of this population who do not become addicted to be abnormal. Yes, not becoming addicted when most people do could be viewed as a dysfunction, a disorder because it goes against the majority. A dysfunction not to become addicted! This sounds rather silly, doesn't it? But that is exactly what we are doing when we look at those with addictions as having a dysfunction or a disorder instead of an illness. The truth is, they are responding to the substance exactly the way they were built or made to respond – they are simply genetically predisposed.

I know this heroin analogy may sound a bit ridiculous, but is it really? Isn't it only natural for people to pride themselves on their ability to control their use? Men really go for this one: drink like a man; real men can control their liquor, etc. However, this ability to control one's use of drink may only be a gift from above. It's just like those people who pride themselves on being attractive and having exceptionally good looks, when in fact, they had nothing to do with it. They were born with those genes. Having control over substance use and having good looks is, in essence, the same thing; neither is totally self-made.

The point is, it is only natural for people to place themselves above others. However unintentional, this is exactly the message being sent and received by patients in treatment when we refer to addiction as being a dysfunction or disorder – instead of an illness, as it rightfully is.

INTERRUPTING DEVELOPMENT

At this point, you may be asking yourself, what's the big deal about the likelihood of biological *causation* – what does it matter if all three biopsychosocial factors play a role in the *development* and progression of addiction anyway? Well, it is immensely important. It is through the understanding of biological causation that addicts can develop a sound reason for staying sober. When recovery is based on the perspective of personal causation, it is *always* shaky at best; "If they can cause it, they can un-cause it." This is the resounding message playing in the minds of all those who desperately want to find any possible way to use again, those with addictions. Addicts must fully comprehend their biological reaction to use and internalize the impact of this information - that they never really had any control over their addiction in the first place, and therefore, they will never be able to control their use in the future. This critical understanding becomes their reason for staying sober and the motivation they need to address all the psycho-emotional and social-environmental repercussions of their addiction. Eventually, this knowledge will provide them with an unwavering foundation to a new life.

This is what appears to be missing from so many treatment programs – a *foundation* on which to build a long, stable, and lasting sobriety – the reason why they not only developed an addiction, but why they can never go back to using, even after many years of sobriety. Mental-emotional health does not make anyone more or less resistant to biological adaptation. This is why addressing all the psychological and social aspects of addiction, without establishing a foundational *reason* for why they developed an addiction in the first place, can lead addicts to a misconception of their condition. This is why an adherence to the psychosocial perspective of causation is likely to result in more denial and increased guilt and shame. This, of course, leads to continued *slips* (one time using episodes) and *relapses* (right back into addiction).

As it is, addicts usually have their own conception of what addiction is when they come into treatment, and for most of them, they really do not believe they are addicts in the first place. For the majority, regardless of how severely affected, still believe they could control their use if they only wanted to (for this is what the psychosocial perspective of causation promotes). They are completely oblivious to the fact that their *wanting-to-use* is the addiction. This is where treatment should start, and this is where biological vulnerability could be put to good use.

When we understand that chemical addictions are the direct result of individual responses to the effects of chemicals on the brain, and successfully translate this knowledge to the patient, they can begin to see the driving force behind their use; that their desire-to-use (addiction) was not of their own making; and that it was more likely due to biological, psychological, and social-environmental adaptations to the effects of the drug they became addicted to. It is at this point we can *then* help to empower them in overcoming all their biopsychosocial adaptations, and intervene anywhere along the development of addiction. We do not have to wait until they reach devastating states of despair.

For example, I recall working with a well-educated man who had not experienced much loss as a result of his use. He had never been to treatment but was getting negative feedback from his wife about his excessive partying. A friend of his had referred him to me and we spent an hour or so going over the details of his use. He was undoubtedly in the early grips of addiction. One week later we met for another hour. In this second session I explained to him what addiction was and why only some people were so affected; that they could not control their use no matter how much they would like to. I told him that if he had this condition, which appeared to be the case, he would either have to find a way to remain abstinent, or continue along the best he can until the consequences of his use became too unbearable. He was still at the point where he could control whether or not he drank when he was sober, but could not control how much, or for how long he drank once he started. I informed him that addictions only get worse and never better; that according to his symptoms, it would be extremely likely that he would sooner or later lose all control over his drinking. Then I gave him one of my exercise packets to complete and told him to give me a call the following week to set up another session. He never called that third week. However, I did hear from him about two years later.

This is when he had told me what he had done. He said he had called to let me know how good he was doing and how grateful he was for the information I had shared with him. He told me how this information had helped him to seek help and remain sober. This was amazing. The mere fact of knowing what his condition was, that he was able to identify it, and that it was not of his own making, nor his fault, fully aware that he had no control over what his use was doing to him, prompted him to seek help through the mutual support group known as AA and find recovery. He also informed me that his relationship with his wife and family had become more rewarding than ever. His rather instant and complete turnaround is extremely rare. However, it does suggest just how powerful this information can be when it is applied appropriately.

This example shows that when addiction is viewed as an unavoidable reaction to use for those who are highly vulnerable to a substance's effects and adaptations, it is much easier for people to accept. This is what can make treatment much more effective. It can allow us to reach people well before all the psychological and emotional damage sets in.

This part of addiction, the psycho-emotional damage, is likely to be the result of what is known as cognitive dissonance. Cognitive dissonance is when one's behavior is in conflict with one's perception of self and their values. When this occurs, it leads to an increase in cognitive distortions, self-condemnation, low self-esteem, and increased anxiety and depression, etc. It is very likely to be the reason for most all of the mental and emotional distress associated with those having a chemical addiction. Certainly there are psychosocial influences involved in the development of addictions; however some biological vulnerability must be present for psychosocial issues to have an impact and play a role in the development of chemical addictions.

When I realized how effective the knowledge of biological vulnerability was, I went out and asked a few counselors working in the field if they were using the videos created in 2007 by the National Institute on Drug Abuse (NIDA), in collaboration with HBO, called, *Addiction; Why Can't They Just Stop.* These videos emphasize the biological components of addiction. I was told that, although they had them, they did not use them because they saw no value in them. This reiterated what I had already heard.

When I was in college, I can recall one of my professors instructing the class to stay away from the biological factors of addiction. His explanation for this advice was based on the fact that one's biological response to a substance could not be altered. He said, "Someday this may be possible, but not as of yet, so do not go there." At the time, this sounded like some pretty good advice; however, today we have a lot more evidence and there is a major problem with avoiding what our biological evidence has to offer. If we do not "go there," the only two aspects of addiction to place any amount of emphasis on are the psychological and social factors. Doing this, although not directly stated, sends the message that addictions are the result of psychological determinants. Leaving the biological factors out of treatment tells patients that their addiction is the result of poor mental health, a lack of cognitive abilities, or just the poor attitude of choosing to use, and thus, self-imposed. This, apparently, is supposed to motivate addicts into changing their *using behavior* (for that is what the psychological approaches are all about); however, it only makes them feel worse about themselves and sparks more resistance.

In addition to this motivational reason for ignoring the use of biological factors in treatment, there appears to be a universal fear among counselors in the field of exonerating the addict; i.e., if addicts were informed about the likelihood of having a highly vulnerable reaction to their drug (and thus, their addiction not necessarily being their *fault*), they would use this information to continue along their destructive path, free of any guilt or shame, and fall deeper and deeper into their addiction. This is a nice logical assumption, and I understand the concern here; however, there is plenty of evidence to support the contrary.

In fact, it was the use of biological differences which led Bill Wilson and Dr. Bob to start Alcoholics Anonymous (AA). Back in the early 1930s, when Bill Wilson was struggling with his addiction, he eventually came across a physician who described his reaction to alcohol as *something like an allergy* – that what occurs in alcoholics when they drink is something quite different than what happens in *the average temperate drinker.* His name was William D. Silkworth, M.D. This hit home for Bill. It was an explanation he could finally accept and it was so important to him it became the first step in AA's program of recovery – "We admitted we were powerless over alcohol… (p. 59). This came from the knowledge of the allergy. So, when it came to publishing their program of recovery, that the first 100 members had laid out in the book, *Alcoholics Anonymous,*

Bill went to Dr. Silkworth and requested a letter of support, which Dr. Silkworth was pleased to supply; however, there was no mention of the allergy in it. This was a very nice letter, and full of support for Bill and Bob's program, but it did not serve their purpose. They needed a confirmation of the allergy from a medical professional, not just the hearsay of two alcoholics – for they knew this would not be accepted. So, they returned to Dr. Silkworth in pursuit of his written medical opinion – that alcoholism is "…a manifestation of an allergy; that the phenomenon of craving is limited to this class…" of drinker, which Dr. Silkworth supplied in his second letter. (AA, 2001, p. xxviii) This information was so important it was placed in the very beginning of the book. If it were not for *The Doctor's Opinion* it is very unlikely that AA would have even gotten off the ground, much less become the huge success it is today.

In AA, the use of this biological perspective has proven its effectiveness in helping millions upon millions of alcoholics over the past eighty years. Members base their recovery on having a biological reaction to alcohol. This is reflected in their 1st step of being *powerless* over [the *effects* of] alcohol, and that control can only be gained through complete abstinence. If anyone doubts that this is the stance of the original members, consider this one quote from their book: "Can it be appreciated that he has been a victim of crooked thinking, directly *caused* by the action of alcohol on his brain?" (Alcoholics Anonymous, 2001, p.140)

This does not mean that we should ignore or minimize the psychological and social aspects of addiction; it only means that biological vulnerability can be used much more effectively, and that it has been missing from the professional side of treatment for far too long. It also appears to be quite effective in reaching those who have not been severely devastated by their addiction; those with much higher "bottoms."

It's time for a change, and today we have all the evidence we need. The biological causation of addiction is so well accepted by the scientific field of medicine that scientists are now working on ways to identify truly at-risk individuals through genetic mapping. Whether or not some people are more biologically prone to addiction is not even a question, *this is a known fact today*. Yet, this information is still sitting on the shelf collecting dust. It is not being disclosed or effectively applied in most treatment facilities.

Some of this resistance to the proper use and application of our biological evidence may stem from what are known as "risk factors" for addiction. These are commonly used to identify developmental factors in addictions; however, they are actually of no useful value. Risk factors are a list of traits and conditions found in the life-course experiences of *those who have already been found to have an addiction*. And since risk factors for addiction are only obtained from those with addictions and who are likely to already possess a greater degree of biological vulnerability (for they became addicted), risk factors can only be used when they are applied to other people with greater degrees of biological vulnerability - those with addictions. Therefore, we cannot apply the social and behavioral risk-factors we see in addicts to everyone, such as the use of various substances, poverty, and having authoritative parents, because they do not apply to everyone – they only apply to those known to have an addiction. In other words, these so-called risk factors are pretty much good for nothing. Let's elaborate.

With these so-called risk-factors, we need to remember that correlation (seeing this with that) does not determine causation. There can be many other explanations for why we see common traits among addicts. For example, most addicts are relatively poor. In this case, the presumptuous risk factor would be poverty. However, just because we see a lot of poverty among addicts, this does not mean that poverty causes addiction. It is more likely that addiction causes poverty. All this so called risk-factor of poverty tells us, is that many people with addictions (for this was the sample) experience poverty. So, to try and use them to predict who will and won't develop addictions, among a whole population, is a misapplication of research. In fact, they should not be called risk-factors at all because they are not a very accurate predictor of risk.

Comparing the development of chemical addictions to the development of type-II diabetes is another way to comprehend the uselessness of risk factors. For example, some of the risk factors for type-II diabetes are: having a family history of diabetes, excessive consumption of sugar and being 10 to 20 lbs. overweight; however, most people who possess these same risk factors will never develop this disease. This is because of the way risk factors are acquired, being gathered only from those known to have this disease. Likewise, not everyone with so called risk factors for addiction is actually at risk for addiction, regardless of whether or not they abuse drugs. This is because not all people who abuse drugs become addicted; there must also be some degree of biological vulnerability for an addiction

Part One: A Call for Change

to develop. In the case of alcohol, no matter how much some may drink, most of them will never develop alcoholism. The well-known fact that most college students who abuse alcohol for years while they are in college never develop alcoholism confirms this to be a fallacy. Therefore, the abuse of alcohol as the *cause* of alcoholism (for everyone) is purely a myth perpetuated by personal beliefs.

Since everyone is likely to have a different level of biological vulnerability to alcohol, no one can use risk-factors to accurately predict who will and who won't develop alcoholism. The bottom line is just this; no one can make themselves an alcoholic without a genetic predisposition to alcohol; just like no one can acquire type-II diabetes without a genetic predisposition to type-II diabetes.

Ideally, the best way to avoid the development of any addiction would be to never use drugs that are known to be addictive. However, this is rather unrealistic, especially in the modern culture of drug use today. Although encouraging children, teens, and young adults to stay away from them is the best prevention, we still need additional strategies. The second best thing may be to teach them how to recognize abnormal reactions to use that may indicate a biological vulnerability. Scientists have already identified several specific gene sets known to be associated with various chemical addictions, like alcohol, nicotine, and opiates, but we still do not have any inexpensive or practical way to go about testing large populations. Until then, all we have to go on is an abnormal reaction to use – the intense effects and responses to use, such as loss-of-control and distinct behavioral changes. Educating our younger population with the knowledge of bio-

114

logical vulnerability creates a much better chance of reaching those vulnerable and giving them a chance to take responsibility for their condition well before experimentation develops into addiction. Merely telling children that using causes addiction, which is an exaggeration of the truth, and telling them not to use drugs, especially when they see others using drugs e.g., parents who drink, (and without consequences I might add) does absolutely no good. Children, like most people, may be ignorant about the risks of using various drugs, but they have the intelligence to understand what genetic predisposition is. However, better education for our children will never materialize until the profession changes its stance on causational beliefs and recognizes the usefulness and benefits of biological vulnerability; which, until now, has been denied its proper place in the biopsychosocial model of addiction.

It is imperative to give these issues serious consideration. I realize some of it may be hard to stomach, especially for those who have been in the field for a long time, but I do hope to encourage those who may still be harboring some doubts to keep an open mind and focus on the benefits I am proposing. I have no doubt that the acceptance of biological vulnerability will not only improve treatment outcomes, but also reduce the rates of addiction as a whole, as well as reduce the rates of relapse among those receiving treatment. Sometimes we have to unlearn what we think we know to make room for new knowledge, and this may be our greatest challenge. In the next few chapters we will examine more reasons why change is so desperately needed.

RECOVER -
"To get back - to bring
back to normal position
or condition"
- Merriam-Webster (2000)

Chapter 6

Recovery

Causational perspectives also affect and have an impact on the conception of what recovery is and what is required to achieve it. The psychosocial perspective views recovery as *maintaining* abstinence through continuous vigilance, and the biological view is that recovery is an *obtainable* release from the desire-to-use, the addiction. Each one stems from a *belief* on how and why only some people become addicted in the first place. Although both perspectives may be useful in gaining progress in recovery, the concept of endless maintenance, although widely accepted in treatment communities around the world, may not be the best solution. Vigilance in maintaining abstinence is needed while one is actually in-recovery; however, and at some point, people can and do fully recover.

The reason I am addressing this issue is because it not only affects one's hope that their suffering will eventually cease and be over, but that it may also affect one's self-image, and therefore, hinder their recovery. There are many in recovery who believe that they are mentally incapable of controlling their use because they are in some way mentally or emotionally impaired, either from birth, childhood trauma, or brain damage from excessive use, and then there are those who just accept the permanency of their biological reaction to a substance. These two types of recovery depend on what they believe, and their beliefs are acquired through what they learn in treatment.

Clearly, a recovery based on maintaining a certain level of mental and emotional well-being is a contingent recovery – meaning, as long as mental health is maintained one can remain sober. If mental health falters, one is again placed at risk for relapse. This concept is based on how well one can cope with all of life's little ups and downs. It stems from the psychosocial perspective of causation; for if a lack of mental health caused you to turn to substance use in the first place, and you recover through improved mental health, then obviously this level of improved mental health must be maintained. Although this concept makes a lot of sense, it is concerning because it suggests recovery can never be trusted, for the challenges of life are too unpredictable. This is clearly a <u>conditional</u> recovery, which is commonly referred to as *in-recovery*. How defeating and hopeless is this? Would you like to be referred to as the person in-recovery for the rest of your life, just because you once had an addiction, especially with the stigma that is so closely associated with it? Doesn't this terminology, in-recovery, come along with the implication that there is something that is just not right about you? Who would want that?

On the other hand, if we realize that addiction is actually caused by the drug, and not the person, then any attempt to use *safely* ever again would be just as impossible as it was in the first place, and this is much easier for addicts to comprehend and accept. It is actually more reflective of one's own experience. When this is clearly understood and accepted by the person seeking recovery, they can begin to realize they did not have much of a say in the development of their addiction. This is such an important point I cannot stress it enough. It eliminates any idea that they became an addict as a result of what others might have done, life challenges, or any lack of mental fortitude on their part. What was going to happen happened because of their genetic propensity toward their drug of use. This perspective not only frees the person from all the guilt and shame associated with having an addiction, but it extinguishes the tendency to blame their addiction on others, such as: parents, spouses, friends, employers, God, and even the world in which they live, not to mention the self-pity that is sure to follow. They finally realize they have a condition that they can never change, no matter how much they would like to, ever. This removes any conscious or unconscious thoughts or desires of ever using safely again and provides them with an <u>unconditional</u> basis for their recovery. Regardless of what life throws out, to fully understanding the biological permanency of their condition actually empowers addicts to face their struggles head on, without the use of drugs, and this is where their real growth and psycho-emotional repair starts to occur. This is what leads them "back to normal position or condition" (Merriam, 2000) – true recovery.

Through the understanding of biological vulnerability, one can obtain a rewarding recovery once and for all. This is known as being *recovered* (a term used in the book of AA), rather than being in-recovery forever. Yes, there is a little more to it, like learning to appreciate and enjoy life as a sober person, but once the peace, joy, and serenity of recovery is gained through group therapy and personal growth, the addict is no longer plagued with the desire-to-use; there is too much gratitude for the freedom they have achieved for any of life's tragedies and challenges to shake them. *This is because using is never an option.* This is an unconditional recovery because, unlike the psychosocial perspective, it does not depend on maintenance. Knowledge of their condition and an undeniable *belief* that they are vulnerable is all they need. To those who have recovered, their condition is just as much of a fact to them as the color of their hair. It becomes part of their new identity. For those allergic to strawberries, there is no need to keep eating strawberries to know they are still allergic, nor do they have to practice any kind of spiritual life to stay away from them. Once they know, they just know. This is how it is for the many who have indeed recovered.

Patients need to know they can overcome their addiction once and for all. Some addicts remain abstinent with no attention given to maintenance what-so-ever; it appears that in the changing of their attitude toward substance use, their way of viewing life, adopting new and positive coping strategies, and in finding new ways of enjoying life, they just remain abstinent on their own without any, or very little, effort at all. These are fully recovered addicts. They have told me that they know that it was their unique response to their drug that *caused* their addiction, nothing else. Isn't it time we listen?

On the other hand, the psychosocial perspective conveys a message of endless maintenance, robbing people of any hope of full and complete recovery. When addicts get into recovery on the belief that they are mentally or emotionally impaired, their recovery is always shaky at best. First, their recovery is based on the *condition* that they do certain things to support and *maintain* their recovery; they are led into believing that if they falter, they would be placing themselves at risk for relapse. They may also remain abstinent for a multitude of other reasons such as: avoiding more consequences, keeping employment, keeping the family together, finding love, getting their spouse back, etc. I remember hearing one man's life story in which he remained abstinent for over twenty years on a promise he had made to his wife; that he would not drink again until he retired from work, which he kept. However, without a biological understanding of his condition, this did not work out very well for him and he found himself back in treatment at the age of 65. Personally, I don't know how he did it for all those years. He must have been tormented by what he really wanted (his drug) for all those years, never knowing his response to alcohol was really beyond his control in the first place. Obviously he did not believe in genetic predisposition because I remember him saying that he truly believed that he was finally mentally and emotionally healthy enough to drink again after all those years. *What this man failed to realize is that his mental and emotional health had nothing to do with his ability to control his use;* for him, it was indeed a biological response.

I have literally heard hundreds and hundreds of conditional recoveries like this one. It appears that when addicts recover on the belief that they are in some way mentally or emotionally impaired, or damaged, they inevitably believe they must maintain their recovery for the rest of their life; that they must control their desire-to-use indefinitely. They have been taught, and therefore believe, that their illness is always calling them, lurking in the dark like a cancer patient in remission. This is sad, but this is what is promoted by the way addiction is currently viewed and addressed. This belief in having to maintain one's recovery indefinitely is clearly based upon the psychosocial perspective of *causation*.

While incorporating the biological perspective into the psychosocial perspective, something had to give and the only aspect of biological causation that fit nicely into this perspective was biological *adaptation*, so this was easily accepted and different *effects* were left out. Adaptation, which is presented as the damage caused by drug use, is the explanation for why those who once appeared to have control over their use, no longer could, even after mental and emotional repair. The problem is, most addicts do not believe that they damaged their brains to such an extent, to the point of never being able to use again. However, there are reasons for this non-belief, and basically, it just does not sit right with them. At some level, all addicts know there is a biological calling behind their desire-to-use and when their cravings are gone (due to the brain returning to normal through abstinence), there is nothing left to stop them from trying to use again. Damage to the brain caused by the excessive use of a drug fits nicely into the psychosocial perspective, but as you can see, it is only a half-truth that is not very effective. For, it does not provide an acceptable answer for why addicts can never use again; and therefore, it is too easy for addicts to deny; which, of course, given any chance at all, they will take. This has nothing to do with denying the addiction, it is all about a lack of belief. They just do not believe that they are permanently mentally incapable of controlling their use, and under this perspective, there is no proof for them to *believe* in.

On the other hand, the biological perspective does offer the proof needed to gain *belief.* It has always been accepted that biological cravings dissipate and disappear in time with abstinence, but today we have evidence of it through brain imaging and animal studies. Today we know that the brain actually does repair itself. To what extent we do not yet know, but it does explain why some addicts experience physical urges and cravings for years after cessation (stopping), which eventually do subside. The theory is that neurological chemicals and receptors return to normal in time. This contradicts the idea that brain damage from excessive use *causes* addiction. For if it did, would not the brain repair these structures as well? If so, would they not have the possibility of controlling their use again someday? Could they not learn to use more moderately in the future? It surely didn't for the retired man with over twenty years of sobriety. Does it not make better sense that if the drug caused addiction in the first place, it would do it again and again, even after twenty years of sobriety?

Biological predisposition explains why an addict can never use safely again — because they never really could to begin with.

So, what is full-recovery, and how does one obtain it? Full-recovery is being released from the desire-to-use; which, as I have been saying all along, is the addiction. This is accomplished through abstinence and the knowledge of where the desire-to-use stems from, a biological reaction to a drug. When patients finally recognize this and fully accept their condition, they have been given the explanation for why they loved their drug so much and why they couldn't let go of it. This is a relief unto its own. It will no longer exist to plague them because the option to use has been removed.

Having this knowledge and belief in biological causation motivates clients to get rid of all the driving forces behind their desire-to-use – all the psychological and social adaptations that have sprung up in response to having had a biological need to use. For they come to learn how these psychosocial adaptations will continue to tempt and torment them from time to time if they are not addressed and overcome, even after the biological urges have subsided.

Knowing that recovery can be obtained provides patients with the hope they most desperately need. Addiction must be faced head-on, not avoided or suppressed. Those who gain this type of recovery are no longer plagued with the desire-to-use because, biologically speaking, there is no possibility of ever gaining control over their use, and they know this. Once addicts finally realize, and accept, these two truths: (1) use ignites the desire-to-use, and (2) there is no possibility of ever controlling their use, then they are finally equipped with a **foundation** on which to build a solid and *unconditional* recovery. Yes, there is more to it, like finding peace, joy, and happiness through personal growth, but more importantly, they finally realize that their addiction was not the result of any mental inadequacies, but in fact, a biological reaction. What a relief this is for them. This benefit of biological causation is indisputable.

Through this unconditional recovery, ex-addicts eventually realize that they are just as normal as anyone else, as long as they don't use. They know they can't use like other people and they know why – what is, is. They just accept this fact as they would any other condition that requires a restriction of diet (diabetes, allergies, obesity, hypertension, etc.). This fact does wonders for one's self-esteem. Instead of tearing down one's self-image and pressuring clients into believing that they are in some way responsible for their condition, or that they are mentally or emotionally impaired, or any other reason in order to help them, the truth about biological vulnerability is very empowering.

On the other hand, when it is taught and accepted that the only way to remain sober takes the continued maintenance of one's mental, emotional, and spiritual well-being, it robs patients of any real hope of complete recovery. It actually sends a message of hopelessness; not only will they always be plagued with thoughts and yearnings to use, supposedly due to a poor level of mental and emotional health, but they will adopt a poor self-image and live in fear of relapse. I have heard people in AA with over 20 years of sobriety stating that they must still come to meetings every day because they know they are "just not right" – to these folks, alcoholic means permanently ill, something they must treat till the day they die or they will invariably drink again. Although one could say this is working for them, I find this quite disturbing.

I have found that when addicts recover on the knowledge of their biological condition, slips and occasional use rarely, if ever, develop into full-blown relapse. Each slip (one using episode) appears to only reinforce the fact of their biological condition and strengthen their resolve never to use again. However, I would like to make it perfectly clear that just having this knowledge about biological vulnerability will not keep an addict sober. They must also learn new ways of coping with life's struggles and gain a love for their new found sobriety. Getting over a love affair with a drug takes time. It is not much different than a divorce from a spouse. In fact, it may even be a little harder. Addicts learn, either consciously or unconsciously, that their drug was the only thing on God's green earth that they could depend on absolutely – it never let them down because it always made them feel better, even when they were not feeling low. So, getting over this love affair can take any number of months or years, and I suspect the time it would take for one to fully recover would depend on one's individual degree of addiction at the time of treatment and the degree of personal growth one can aspire to. This takes a lot of work in practicing honesty and humility, especially with one's self.

The misconception of having to practice recovery for the rest of one's life appears to exist for two main reasons: first, it explains why most patients in and out of treatment relapse (but, could this be a response to the feelings of incompetence that Dr. Sander referred to in his book?); and secondly, it is a misapplication of biological permanence. The statement, "Once an addict, always an addict" is true in reference to biological responses to a particular substance, which appears to never change. However, as I have previously brought to your attention, this does not mean the addiction (the desire-to-use) is permanent, just the biological response to the drug.

Clients can and do fully recover when they understand *where* their addiction stems from – that the loss-of-control, urge, and desire-to-use comes from the drug. Once an addiction has been addressed and overcome (research suggests ½ to 1½ years for biological recovery, and 1 to 3 years for psychological recovery), it should no longer be an issue for any recovered addict. In other words, the amount of diligence, thought, and effort put into maintaining recovery becomes almost nonexistent. This would be the *termination phase* of Prochaska's & DiClemente's stages of change (Spokane County, PDF). This misunderstanding of recovery is why you will probably never hear about this stage of change in clinical treatment. It has apparently been discarded to conform to misconceptions about recovery, which, of course, stem from the psychosocial perspective and its insistence upon personal accountability – the same way most all mental health issues are addressed. Remember the words of Irvin Yalom in chapter 3? – "Knowingly or unknowingly, the need for taking responsibility underlies nearly every therapeutic [psychological] intervention?"

It is true that many recovered addicts do things to maintain their satisfaction with life, but this is because they have gained a new appreciation for life and insist on enjoying it. It is also true that self-improvement and growth provides a reassurance against relapse, but it really has little to do with remaining sober. It is all about remaining happy and satisfied. Just the mere act of remaining sober is inadequate for those who have suffered the tortures of addiction. For those who have been there, and have suffered the "gut wrenching cries of the soul," experiencing a life free from this torment is just too rewarding for them to ignore.

In reference to the book, *Alcoholics Anonymous,* once again, recovered alcoholics would no more pick up a drink than put their hand on a hot stove. Would you put your hand on a hot stove? I bet the thought of it never crosses your mind, right? And so, the thought of ever using again rarely crosses the minds of recovered addicts, and if it does periodically, it is dismissed as quickly as any other foolish thought. Just like "normal" people, recovered addicts are not tempted to hurt themselves. There is absolutely nothing wrong with their minds. Find any ex-smoker and ask them what they do to remain smoke free and I bet their answer will be something like, "Absolutely nothing, I just refuse to smoke." It is the same for recovered addicts. Just like having one cigarette will lead most ex-smokers right back into their addiction (because of the biological reaction), so would one use for most addicts in recovery, and they know this all too well. This is what keeps them sober – the fact that they know this; not anything they do or fail to do. I repeat, they are not in remission from a disease like cancer, lurking in the dark and waiting to reemerge at any unforeseeable time; they have found that they are in control of their addiction as long as they remain sober. Like the ex-smoker, only through the knowledge of what caused their addiction are they finally able to take control of it.

I was amazed to find that so many addicts in and out of treatment lacked any real belief about the how or why of their condition. They certainly knew what others believed, but it was obvious to me that they really did not believe very much of it for themselves. Sobriety is built upon belief and unless we can give them something solid to believe in they will continue to rebel and struggle with recovery. This is why so many of them, even after repeated bouts of incarceration and treatment, still refuse to believe they have a problem with alcohol or drugs. For addicts who can remain abstinent, without a firm and solid causational belief, the addiction, the desire-to-use, can lie dormant for years upon years and continue to torment its host (the addict) from time to time. This is the difference between being *in-recovery* indefinitely, where one is occasionally plagued with the desire-to-use, and being *recovered* where the desire-to-use has been replaced with a joy and gratitude for life. The biological perspective not only assists in this transformation, but in all the steps along the way.

Chemical addictions are not all the same; what it takes for one person to recover from an addiction may be much greater than what it may take for another. Not all addicts face the same challenge. Some are more addicted than others, and they will have a harder fight; however, if they fully recover, neither of them will have to *maintain* a recovery program for life, nor will they have to carry the stigma of addiction on their back. Their addiction will be over. This is the great message of biological vulnerability – that complete restoration is possible; that an addict can once again be normal.

KNOWLEDGE -
"...apprehending truth or fact
through reasoning...
the sum of what is known"
- Merriam-Webster (2000)

Chapter 7

Knowledge

Through evidence of biological predisposition we possess the answers to most, if not all, the puzzling and perplexing questions posed to us by chemical addictions, and yet this knowledge still remains unused. Because of this, many patients are completing treatment and being discharged without a very good understanding of their condition. What is most disturbing to me is that most of them do not believe they are really addicts even after inpatient and outpatient services. They are not even equipped to answer some of the most basic and essential questions of their condition, and as far as I know, no other disease is treated quite like this. Today, through scientific research, we can now provide them with some very good answers to their most basic and relevant questions:

- What is addiction?
- What causes addiction?

- Why do some people become addicted and others do not?
- Why can't addicts ever use again?
- Why can't addicts use other psychotropic drugs?
- Why don't all people with mental or emotional problems become addicts?
- Why don't all trauma victims become addicts?
- Why do movie stars and successful people become addicts?

There seems to be no end to the list of questions I have heard from patients recently discharged from treatment. The biggest one for me was – how can some of these patients go through four or five outpatient programs, and numerous inpatient stays without learning much of anything? What is wrong with our current modes of treatment? And, more importantly, what can we do to improve this?

One way is to provide our clients with answers. I believe the perspective of biological vulnerability will improve treatment outcomes because it brings the complexity of addiction into focus. In presenting evidence-based research and facts, without bias, we can provide clients with the knowledge they need to effectively address their condition. It is through knowledge that addicts can identify and more readily accept their condition, which is the most important step in obtaining recovery. The biological and epigenetic perspectives address all the questions above with answers that are much more palatable than what the psychosocial perspective has to offer. The psychosocial perspective can only provide answers to what is seen, such as addiction being the continued use of a chemical substance despite harmful consequences. This is nothing new to the addict, they already know this. Most addicts have been dealing with consequences for many years before they even enter treatment. What they need to know is, "What is addiction?" Is it just self-destructive behavior, as the psychosocial perspective promotes, or is there more to it? This is why I suspect the issue of causation is currently avoided like the plague, and why so many addicts are continuing to leave treatment utterly confused and with no readily acceptable answers to their questions. I am not saying that biological vulnerability is the only cause of addiction here, a decline in mental health surely plays its part: what I am saying is that it can provide desperate addicts with real answers. According to the biological perspective, *addiction is a biological reaction to a chemical substance,* a reaction in the brain that is out of anyone's control; a reaction that keeps addicts trapped in the cycle of using.

As far as for what causes addiction, this goes hand in hand with what a chemical addiction actually is. Biologically speaking, we can acknowledge that addiction stems from the *effects* of drugs on the brains of those who are more vulnerable to what the drug can do to them, such as providing effects so intensely pleasurable, they are bound to return for more, regardless of any consequences that may result. These effects are so strong that once an addict starts using they cannot stop and the drug takes over all mental control. This happens over and over again until the host of the drug (the person) develops physical dependence from repeated exposure and the body actually needs the drug. This is the result of neurological adaptations occurring in the brain as the body tries to regain stability (homeostasis) but cannot. *So, to answer the question of what causes addiction, it is most surely the drug.* The psychosocial perspective claims otherwise; it states addiction is caused by a plethora of psychological difficulties. Importantly, even though psychosocial elements play a part in the development of addiction, scientific evidence tells us that they *only* play a part in those susceptible to the drug's effects. Thus, chemical addictions are actually caused by the drug, which can literally suck those who are unsuspecting right into its trap.

As for why only some people become addicted while others do not, the answer is pretty obvious; some people are just more impacted by the drug than others. Remember what Abraham Lincoln had to say about it? That he lacked the thirst for drinking that he sees in others. Research and evidence are telling the same story, that everyone is a little different when it come to the effects of drugs upon them. *It is clear that genetic differences account for why some people develop chemical addictions and others do not.* However, if people were able to recognize what drugs can do to them, and only them, by utilizing the knowledge of biological vulnerability, fewer people would fall into the vicious and unsuspecting trap of addiction.

Why is it that recovered addicts can never use again? Contrary to what the psychosocial perspective promotes, this is not attributed to irreversible adaptations (damage) to the brain, but rather to the initial effects of the substance on the brain to begin with (just like the power of nicotine on the smoker). It is this response to the chemical in question that causes addiction in the first place. Even if the brain totally heals, which may or may not be possible, it is the addictive response to the drug that will never change. Addiction stems from an allergic type of reaction where the drug has an unusually high impact on brain structures (in those susceptible). It is just like having an allergic skin reaction to any number of substances. Even after the rash heals, the person still has the allergy. Drug addiction is no different and this is why a recovered addict can never use safely again. Just like in the case of an allergy, addicts must still stay away from the substance of their addiction to avoid another outbreak. A person's response to a psychotropic substance is based on their uniquely individual biological reaction; their genetic makeup. This is why some people are repulsed by the effects of marijuana, and why others love it. *The biological reaction, not the result of use (damage), is why recovered addicts can never use again.* What caused addiction in the first place will cause it over and over again.

Recovered addicts cannot indulge in the use of other psycho-tropic substances for three reasons. First of all, all psychotropic substances produce *surges of dopamine* that directly impact the mesolimbic system of the brain (the pleasure center) and this activity will interfere with the brain's ability to heal; thus, hinder the already slow process of returning to "feeling okay" when sober. (Remember the Neurotransmitter Baseline diagram in Chapter Four?) Secondly, since one has already been addicted to a substance, which has most likely damaged the pleasure center of the brain, the *likelihood of becoming addicted to another substance* that affects this same area is increased. It also makes it much more likely that a person in recovery from their primary drug of addiction will return to their first drug of addiction because the use of any mind altering drug will feed their love for an altered state of reality – the "in love with the effects" aspect of addiction. And, lastly, through the development of a primary addiction, psychological and social adaptations to drug use have already been established which makes a person highly likely to exhibit addictive behavior toward the use of other drugs. Addiction is not only a biological response to use; it involves psychological and social adaptations as well. Nothing can be done to change one's biological response to a substance; however, *complete abstinence, in learning to cope with life's challenges sober, is what is needed to heal and recover from all the psycho-emotional damage of addiction.* For most addicts, the use of any psychotropic drug is just replacing one addiction for another.

Although mental and emotional problems can contribute to the development of chemical addictions, they do not actually cause them. We know this because most all people suffering from mental health problems never develop chemical addictions. *Only people who are biologically susceptible to what a psychotropic substance can do to the brain develop addictions.* Now, if a person comes across a substance they are vulnerable to, and also suffers from some mental health problems, they are probably more likely to develop an addiction much quicker and faster than the person who is only bio-vulnerable. Here degrees of biological vulnerability would also play a significant role as well, but as the progression of addiction indicates, all those suffering from addiction will also experience some mental health problems. This is what chemical addictions do to people. They cause mental and emotional distress, all of which need to be addressed in treatment.

Now for the big one, trauma: this is such a big topic in the world of treatment today. There are some psychologists out there that insist that if you look hard and long enough, you will find a traumatic experience in the past of everyone with an addiction – apparently in a search for a logical explanation to why addicts use like they do. And, boy, do addicts like to suck this one up – "finally, an explanation for why I use like I do!" The truth is that traumas, just like mental and emotional problems, have nothing to do with the how or why some people develop chemical addictions and others do not. It still comes back to the person's individual biological reaction to the drug. These explanations may help to comfort the addict, by helping to relieve some of the shame and guilt associated with having an addiction; however, even if they are addressed and overcome, like they should be, this will not resolve the addiction. As we have learned, addiction is something entirely different, and any addicted trauma victim who is lucky enough to overcome their traumatic experience, will still not be able to go out and take part in the recreational use of their drug. And, I do believe that if you look long and hard enough you will find a traumatic experience in the past of every human being, addiction or no addiction. Life is like that. What is traumatic for one person might be but a stone in the road for another, but the effects can be just as devastating for both. This is such an important topic right now that I dare not leave it without a warning.

Providing addicts with an excuse for their use, such as to encourage or allow them to blame their addiction on their trauma can have some very detrimental effects. It is actually quite harmful because it makes it far too easy for addicts to start blaming their addiction on other people, experiences, and just plain bad luck (e.g., exaggerated or real child abuse, poverty, wealth, death of a loved one, feeling like they don't fit in, etc.). These excuses may sound rather logical and appropriate, but they only serve to hinder an addict's recovery by fostering feelings of blame and self-pity. In addressing any past traumas, it is therefore vitally important to understand that trauma only contributes to the use of a drug and the development of addiction – only in people who are vulnerable to the effects of the drug in the first place.

I will be elaborating more on the relationship between trauma and addiction later, but what is important to know here is that traumas are just like any other mental health problem, neither can cause addiction without a bio-vulnerability. There are just way too many trauma victims in the world who do not have a chemical addiction for this assumption to hold any weight. However, there is one significant reason why so many people believe that trauma causes addiction – nearly all addicts are victims of trauma. If an addict was lucky enough to escape a traumatic experience before they started using, they most like experienced one after they started. This is because so many addicts behave in such a way, and live a lifestyle, that puts them at a very high risk for being abused and traumatized.

And lastly, why do movie stars and successful people become addicts? Well, there are plenty of reasons, but the biggest one of all is that they are not exempt from biological vulnerability just because they are intelligent and famous. Addiction does not discriminate. Actually, the more successful and wealthy a person becomes, the more susceptible they are to the developmental factors of addiction. There are a multitude of developmental factors that can either contribute to or suppress use (remember drugs cause addiction). So, even if they have a lower level of bio-vulnerability to a particular substance than other addicts, they can actually be more likely to develop an addiction because of their wealth. They are the ones with *more time and resources to feed their addiction*. And, this is why movie stars and successful people are actually more likely to develop addictions. If you remember, biological vulnerability exists on a continuum, from adverse effects to highly intense effects. So, it only stands to reason, if a person is even slightly vulnerable to what drugs can do to them, biologically speaking, then the more access they have to drugs, the more likely they would be to use more and more, which of course, would speed up the development of an addiction.

Knowledge is a wonderful gift and we will be looking into much more of it in Part Two. It is through this knowledge that we are able to dispute the obvious; that addiction is not the result of poor attitudes and inferior mental abilities; that no one can cause themselves to become addicted any more than one can prevent it. Today, we now know, without any doubt, that some people are more susceptible to a variety substances than others, and that this predisposition is based in one's biology. It is through our scientific discoveries that we are now able to peer into the underpinnings of chemical addictions and uncover most of, if not all, the mysteries that have plagued the field of science and addiction for centuries. This knowledge must not go to waste. It must not only be well understood, but consistently and intelligently applied.

Causation is a highly controversial subject, and this is what this book is all about. Many of those in the profession claim that the issue of causation is irrelevant in practice and my goal is to dispel this myth by exposing all the ways in which causation affects treatment in almost every area. In the next chapter, the last of Part One, we will look into all the ways in which the stigma of addiction continues to impact and affect treatment and recovery, as well as how it dictates professional conduct within the field.

STIGMA –
"A mark of shame
or discredit"
– Merriam-Webster (2000)

Chapter 8

Stigma

Why is it, after all these years, and with all our advanced knowledge on addiction, the stigma of addiction continues to thrive? What is the stigma of addiction and how does this stigma affect one's progress in recovery? Do causal perceptions contribute to the stigma of addiction? And, if so, what can be done to lessen its impact on those afflicted and abolish this stigma from society?

The stigma of addiction goes something like this; addiction is a tremendously irresponsible use and abuse of drugs and alcohol; a pathetically despicable display of pure self-indulgence; an habitual escape from reality; something someone brings upon themselves; a result of immature behavior, poor attitudes, and self-pity; a habit that can lead to physical dependence and serious consequences; an obvious reflection of weak character, lack of integrity, and no self-control; and, perhaps most egregious, if addicts really wanted to stop using they could, after all, it's really nothing more than just a bad habit, a poor lifestyle – the result of people behaving badly.

In other words, addiction is thought of as just reward for misbehavior. The point here is that the stigma of addiction is really nothing more than just another causal perception, a perspective; a very critical, unfounded, and judgmental one *based on comparing individual experiences,* not research or evidence.

To lessen the impact stigma has on patients in treatment there has been a movement to strike the word addict from the field of treatment. It is believed by many that the use of phrases like "she is addicted" or "he is chemically dependent" would be much more compassionate, and I agree. The word addict does carry with it the stigma associated with having an addiction – "a mark of shame or discredit" (Merriam-Webster, 2000). However, the stigma is all about causational beliefs and really has nothing to do with the words used to refer to the condition. Whether one calls a person with an addiction an *addict* or a *chemically dependent person* does not lessen the stigma surrounding the condition. For addicts seeking recovery, there comes a time when they must accept their condition, not necessarily the stigma, but separating the two can be very hard. Most addicts come into treatment with a stigmatized view of addiction themselves. For treatment to be successful, acceptance of this highly stigmatized condition cannot be avoided. So, perceptions of what causes addiction can have a huge impact on how long it might take for a person to accept their condition. We can make this easier or harder for them depending on how addiction is viewed and what is being taught, either directly or indirectly, but to strike the word *addict* from the field of addiction might be a really bad idea.

Stigma is such an important issue because it affects every client in treatment. It may be the single greatest barrier to recovery that we know of and the one issue that is not only ignored in most treatment programs, but reinforced through the psychosocial perspective. This is a huge barrier for clients to overcome because, who in their right mind would allow themselves to become an addict if they could find any possible way to avoid it? Addicts, like anyone else, will fight off the possibility of being an actual addict (or a chemically dependent person) with all they have. It is not the label of *addict* they are resisting, it is the *stigma* behind that label they cannot live with, nor accept. This is why most addicts will continue along the progression of the disease/condition until they are forced to reach their "bottom" – the jumping off place.

This is where the insinuation of irresponsible misbehavior and self-causation comes in. Although most counselors in the field of addiction today acknowledge some of the biological components of addiction (as it is almost impossible not to do so), most all of them still hold the addict, at least partially responsible for playing a part in the development of their addiction. In other words, they are only being *partially* stigmatized – and this is in treatment!

Of course, there are some very logical reasons for holding the addict responsible, or even *partially* responsible, which I have already covered, such as addressing addiction as a purely mental health disorder, or attributing 40 to 60 percent of an addiction to psychosocial causes; "it's not your fault, but it is your fault" way of thinking. However, is there really such a thing as *partial* causation? Can one be partially responsible for skin cancer, or the development of type 2 diabetes? Obviously not. Only if they knew they were biologically predisposed to the development of these conditions could they take any steps to prevent them. And, even if they did somehow know, and took precautionary measures, some would still develop these conditions anyway. In other words, there would still be some people so highly vulnerable to these conditions, that no matter what they did, they would still come down with them. It is this same way for addicts. Some people are so highly vulnerable to a specific substance, that once they come in contact with it, nothing is going to stop the development of addiction in that person.

In our world of recreational use, in most developed societies, the message is clear – there is something "wrong" with people who cannot control their use of a psychotropic substance. This is the stigma and this is a real problem, especially in a society where drinking is the norm and control is an expectation. If you are to be a "real" man, you better know how to handle your liquor. So, can you see how devastating it can be for a person, man or woman, to be vulnerable to a substance? Why some of these vulnerable people take it to great depths of despair before accepting help? And, even when they do, how hard it may be for them to accept that they are indeed different, especially when they are made to feel inferior and partially responsible? (As a matter of point, this is probably why there are more male addicts than female addicts)

The sad thing about this is that even though the stigma of addiction has such a profoundly negative impact on a person's ability to accept their condition and seek help, this is not likely to change unless a new perspective of addiction is clinically accepted and applied in treatment. Only through a professional acceptance of biological predisposition, will a new perspective of addiction become socially accepted. Addicts can be taught that addiction is a very real condition, the result of individually unique biological reactions to drugs of use (biological perspective), or they can be taught they did this to themselves as a result of how they chose a using lifestyle (psychosocial perspective). However, which one do you think holds the most potential to be effective? Which one do you think is actually more in line with the truth, and therefore, more accurate? Which one is more in line with the addicts' own experience?

As it is, most treatment providers try to hide their own causational beliefs about addiction from their patients, in believing that addicts are only partially responsible for their addiction. But when this is done, are they not only partially stigmatizing them? Won't their own personal beliefs be conveyed to the patient in one way or another? As I have previously stated, addicts do not lack intelligence; they will pick up on a multitude of seemingly innocent comments and gestures. Professionals, like most people, cannot hide their true beliefs, as they always come out one way or another, and it is the client who feels the brunt of these beliefs, which is still the stigma of addiction. Even partial blame is stigma, and this does not lessen its impact. And, despite this seemingly obvious presence of stigma within the field, the psychosocial perspective is still the most commonly held professional opinion in human services (e.g., physicians, social workers, therapists, counselors, nurses, etc.)

So, how exactly is this stigma reinforced in treatment and what can be done about it? Well, we can tell addicts that their addiction is not really their fault; that given their life's experiences, they were bound to become addicts; that for such and such reasons, they were more likely than others to use like they did – and that this is no excuse for continued use. This helps, but isn't this still the "it's not your fault, but is your fault" insinuation of the psychosocial perspective. It still sends the message that they will eventually have to accept the fact that they did this to themselves if they are ever going to recover. This perspective reinforces the stigma and is actually quite harmful. On the other hand, the biological perspective teaches clients that addiction is an unavoidable result of use for those who are biologically vulnerable. All addicts must find a way to cope with the stigma of addiction, and the biological perspective is much more palpable because it does not require an acceptance of personal-failure. The benefit here is that it helps patients to see past the stigma to what is behind their condition, and that it was never really their own making to begin with. It appears that the use of chemicals to an addict may be just as natural and normal to them as eating, drinking, and breathing is to everyone else. Can you imagine what it must feel like for being stigmatized for fulfilling your needs?

Most treatment providers are quite aware of how the stigma of addiction is a huge barrier to recovery; however, they are blinded to the fact that they are the ones perpetuating it, specifically by the way they view and address addictions. Some providers have implemented the use of the term *chemically dependent* instead of alcoholic or addict, in hopes of relieving some of the stigma; however, this is only a mask. I have to admit, this term does sound much nicer, but in all actuality, it has nothing to do with the stigma of addiction (i.e., irresponsible behavior, mental weakness, character flaw, etc.). It is just another term for the same thing. What's more, the use of the term chemically dependent has not improved treatment outcomes at all. And why would it? In fact, the use of this term may actually be doing more harm than good.

Unless addicts feel they have to use every single day, which most of them don't, they are very unlikely to apply *chemical dependency* to themselves. This gives them a way out, a way to avoid accepting their condition. This is why it may just be better to call a duck a duck, and an addict an addict, than to go around this issue with different terminology. As it is, it is very hard for most addicts to identify their addiction within. Most of them need much help with this and applying another name to the same condition only provides more confusion. It's kind of like a doctor telling their patient they have a hematoma instead of a blood-clot and then having to explain that they are one in the same. There may be good intentions behind the avoidance of the word addict, but in terms of practicality, this is just plain foolishness. Addiction is dependency. The word addict tells us there is a chemical involved; thus, a chemical addiction.

COUNSELOR SELF-DISCLOSURE

For those in disbelief about the stigma of addiction being so prevalent in treatment (and probably why our societal stigma of addiction remains), evidence of it can be seen in how most treatment facilities view a counselor's self-disclosure of a previous addiction. This, like the definition of addiction, has been a topic of much discussion without any universal agreement on the matter. So, is it right or wrong, appropriate or not, for a counselor who has overcome a chemical addiction to disclose this fact to the clients they serve? And, does it matter one way or another? Does it take the focus of treatment off the client, or is it a relevant part of the client's experience and concerns?

Well, if we could all agree upon what addictions are and what causes them, we would be much more inclined to agree upon how to answer these questions. As it is, there is still much disagreement within the field, and as a result, the disclosure of a counselor's previous addiction is usually strongly discouraged, if not outright prohibited.

One explanation given for the discouragement of counselor self-disclosure is that it is believed that no good that can come from it. This is absolutely false. Although a client may not benefit from the *story* of a counselor's using experience, what they do benefit from is the plain fact of the disclosure. For counselors who can disclose a previous addiction, it serves as evidence that they are as normal as anyone else. Clients need this. In this way, they can teach by example that having had an addiction and being vulnerable to what a substance can do to you is nothing to be ashamed of. Used in this way, a counselor need not disclose anything more than the mere fact that they once had an addiction. Such display of honesty can surely help to gain the respect of clients but more important is the value it holds in dispelling the stigma of addiction. However, and this is delicate territory, just like the practice of self-disclosure found in other therapies, too much self-disclosure can lead patients astray and do more harm than good.

Obviously, it does not take a person who has experienced an addiction to treat someone who has one. One of my friend's favorite analogies goes something like this, "If you fell off a boat and were drowning, would you really care who tossed you a rope?" There are just as many very excellent counselors in the field who have never experienced an addiction as those who have. They may have to work a little harder at gaining their clients' trust and respect, but that's only if they are coming from the psychosocial perspective, and this is where the real problem lies.

Applying the biological perspective equips all counselors with the knowledge to gain their clients' confidence and respect whether they have ever experienced an addiction or not. To restrict the use of such a very useful and powerful tool is biased and irresponsible. Despite what is professed, it is not in the best interest of clients. Clients need all the help they can get in overcoming the stigma of addiction and what better way to do this than to present them with counselors who have risen above?

Another reason given for the practice of non-disclosure is to avoid the potential of counselor division. This can occur in many ways. The first one has to do with *client preference*. If some clients know which counselors have experienced an addiction and which ones have not, they may prefer one counselor over another. They may prefer a counselor who has never experienced an addiction over one who has if they want to keep on using and avoid being found out; they may prefer a counselor who has experienced an addiction because they may hold more faith in their abilities and are actually seeking recovery. Or, they may prefer a counselor who has never experienced an addiction over one who has in believing one is healthier than the other. If a patient comes in with the belief that addicts are damaged people, as most do, they are likely to view the counselor who has experienced a previous addiction to be in some way inferior to those who have not. Whatever their reason for counselor preference, this could lead to quite a division between counselors and hinder the treatment team's effectiveness.

This is a very legitimate concern and if there were no other options, non-disclosure would be good policy. However, I suspect the real division between counselors may lie not only in client preference, but in the *different perspectives* these two types of counselors hold and adhere to, which is based on different experiences with various psychotropic drugs. This is where the stigma stems from. Regardless, the bottom line here is that the full acceptance of biological predisposition can put all counselors on the same playing field.

As it is, the practice of counselor disclosure of a previous addiction is a big no-no in most treatment facilities. In others it is absolutely prohibited. The reasons for this practice may sound very reasonable; however, addicts are intelligent and it does not take them long to figure out which counselors have had an addiction and which ones haven't. When they do, it is very likely they will interpret this practice as a sign of shame and disgrace. This does more harm than good because it contributes heavily to the stigma of addiction. Whether intentional or not, it is likely to hinder the recovery efforts of most clients' in treatment.

So, is the self-disclosure of a previous addiction professional or not? Would this personal information help or hinder a client's recovery? Or, does it matter either way? The answers to these questions vary; they are really dependent upon ones' perspective on addiction. Obviously, there are benefits in having recovered counselors working in the field. Using therapeutic terms, they can "come along side" a client's addiction and meet them "where they are at" in ways other counselors may not be able. But what are the implications involved?

First, there are some very effective therapeutic benefits that clients receive from counselors who self-disclose: (1) clients receive a greater confidence in their counselor's ability to help them; (2) it increases the clients' attention and curiosity in the condition itself, which may help them in overcoming ambivalence; (3) it reduces the clients' feelings of inferiority; (4) it utilizes Yalom's therapeutic factors, and at least four of Corsini's nine elements of change; (5) it helps ease clients into greater depths of their own disclosures; (6) it proclaims, by example, that addiction is not something to be ashamed of; (7) it provides a greater sense of hope in the fact that addiction can be overcome; and (8), most importantly, sends the message that recovered addicts are just as normal as anyone else. This may be the healthiest message clients can receive from counselor self-disclosure; however, there are some risks involved if disclosure is not used prudently.

Counselor self-disclosure can be a "double-edged sword." In as much as a counselor's self-disclosure appears to be beneficial (with minimal disclosure – "I am a recovered addict, I have been there too, and I am with you"), it can also hinder the clients' progress if the counselor discloses too much. I have heard well- intentioned counselors preach to clients about how devastating their addiction was, complete with useless and endless stories of grandiosity, and that if they could recover from their extreme depths of addiction then anyone could. This over-disclosure can hinder a client's progress in two very distinct ways. First, it imposes an unrealistic expectation, for everyone's addiction involves different factors. Second, clients will inevitably compare their experience to the counselor's. If they do not think their addiction is as severe as their counselor's they may sink further and further into ambivalence, if not outright denial. Now that we know what the benefits and risks of self-disclosure are, it may be helpful to look at the benefits and costs of non-disclosure.

The benefits of non-disclosure are: (1) it ensures the focus of treatment remains on the patient; (2) it eliminates any risk of counselor over-disclosure; (3) it protects the agency's reputation of professionalism (given the stigma of addiction); and, (4) it can guard against counselor division; and therefore, a treatment team's effectiveness.

The costs of non-disclosure involve: (1) withholding the eight benefits stated above; (2) the risk of exposure, which may be very detrimental to clients who are likely to find out; (3) it sets a very poor example by contradicting the message of truth, honesty, and openness – major tools of successful recovery; (4) it supports the stigma of addiction; and (5), it hinders the development of self-esteem and integrity, which may otherwise be gained through the witness of these characteristics in counselors who do self-disclose.

When comparing the positive and negative implications of counselor disclosure, can we really say that we have the clients' best interest at heart in supporting non-disclosure? Isn't this decision really based on the provider's causational beliefs and their insistence on maintaining it? If I were coming from the belief that addicts caused their own addictions or were in some way inferior to those who never experienced an addiction, I would be much more inclined to support non-disclosure. However, if I were coming from the belief that addictions were the result of an unavoidable biological reaction (for those who are vulnerable to the effects and adaptations of use), that it was a biological condition like any other (anemia, diabetes, etc.) and that there should be no shame or disgrace involved in having such a condition, I would not only support the disclosure of a counselor's previous addiction, I would encourage it.

Obviously, counselor self-disclosure carries with it some very powerful and effective benefits, and there is no legitimate reason why it should not be taken advantage of and put to good use. After all, the success rate of treatment is poor at best. Most would agree that it is in the neighborhood of 2% for first-timers in treatment. With this in mind, can we really justify the withholding any beneficial resource?

PROFESSIONALISM

This brings us back to the question of professionalism. Is it professional for recovered counselors to disclose this fact about themselves to the clients they serve? In reviewing the core values and ethical principles of the helping professions, it is clear that if self-disclosure was to harm clients in any way, such as in the over-disclosure example I just presented, it would definitely be non-professional; however, when responsible self-disclosure enhances and supports clients in recovery, it most surely is professional. In fact, under the guiding principles of beneficence (doing-good) and veracity (truthfulness), it may actually be considered unethical not to do so. Ethically, clients have the right to know about any addiction their counselor has experienced as this is a relevant concern for them. And, regardless of how ill clients may be perceived, they are the consumers of treatment and they deserve the respect of an honest answer.

This concept of illness, leads us right back to the influence causal perspectives have on what addiction is, and what constitutes recovery. It is not unreasonable to conclude that the issue of self-disclosure is really dependent upon one's perspective of addiction. From the avoidable and self-causal view of the psychosocial perspective, it is easy to see how one could view self-disclosure as non-professional, for who in their right mind would support the chronically ill treating others who are ill? But are they? However, from the biological perspective where the condition (response to use) is chronic, not the addiction (the desire-to-use), it would not only be highly appropriate for counselors to self-disclose, it would be a professional responsibility that displays integrity.

Obviously, doctors do not need to have experienced a broken leg, cancer, or any type of disease in order for them to treat their patients. The main difference here is that addiction is a stigmatized condition, and if for no other reason, this is the primary reason self-disclosure of a previous addiction should be encouraged, not discouraged. Counselors who have over-come an addiction to nicotine (a psychoactive substance), free-ly disclose this information to the clients they serve and no one cares. But when a counselor self-discloses a previous drug ad-diction, it's a whole different story. Why is this? Is the discour-agement of counselor self-disclosure of a previous addiction based on evidence, or is it really based on causational beliefs?

In other disciplines, the therapeutic use of counselor self-disclosure is almost always encouraged and practiced by most psychologists. For example, according to Myers & Hayes, 2006, "First, the goal of disclosures should be to enhance or preserve the relationship" (Chang, Scott & Decker, 2009, p. 195). They say it is preferable for counselors to disclose hav-ing had similar struggles and problems, as long as the focus of treatment stays on the patient. For example, "The practitio-ner might say, 'I have some understanding of the challenges you are facing [in] dealing with your mother's illness, because I faced something similar several years ago" (p. 195). In Gestalt Therapy, "...therapists are both permitted and encouraged to disclose their personal experience, both in the moment and in their lives" (Corsini & Wedding, 2008, p. 348). So, why does this practice of non-disclosure appear to be germane to the field of addiction? The only logical explanation I can come up with for this discrepancy is that:

The stigma of addiction is just as alive and well in the field of addiction treatment as it is out in the world.

Clients do not need to know what chemicals were involved in their counselor's addiction to benefit from this knowledge. Just the mere fact that they overcame one, and more importantly, that they are not ashamed of it. This is where the real benefit lies. This is what really matters. In fact, it may be better for clients not to know what substances were involved in their counselor's addiction to eliminate any possibility of comparison. Addiction is addiction; the substance of use is irrelevant. It is the practice of intentionally withholding the truth that appears to be so detrimental; for just the act of it implies and clearly conveys the message of shame. Clients receive this message loud and clear – addiction is something to hide, it is something to rightfully be ashamed of having. After all, they see the professionals doing it! What's worse, is that these professionals are the same people telling them that there is no reason to be ashamed of having an addiction, while at the same time behaving as though they are ashamed of it – by not disclosing whether or not they have ever had an addiction.

EXPERT OPINION

This issue of counselor self-disclosure directly affects the effectiveness of treatment and therefore deserves our attention. Some of the most highly esteemed and recognized professionals of our time, such as Irvin Yalom, Valerie Chang, Raymond Corsini, and Gerald Corey, just to name a few, all support the use of counselor self-disclosure. "Related to being real is the matter of self-disclosure" (Corey, Corey & Corey, 2010, p. 148). Cindy Corey, in her work with refugees from Sudan, states, "If I had maintained a stance of 'no personal self-disclosure,' I doubt that a trusting bond would have developed between us" (Corey, 2010, p. 148). Many others support the use of counselor self-disclosure when it comes to things like: victims of domestic violence, depression, anxieties, aging, bereavement, HIV-AIDS, incest, sexual abuse, rape, compulsive eating, anorexia, etc.

These experts give very clear and distinct explanations for their support of counselor self-disclosure. And they all agree that counselor self-disclosure of a shared experience should not include personal story-telling. There is no therapeutic value in that. Clients can hear stories anywhere. The therapeutic value comes into play when counselors share their feelings, thoughts and behaviors. This is how addicts can be assisted in identifying their own addiction, which is so very hard for them to do. Clearly, self-disclosure is a very important and effective therapeutic tool.

The Benefits of Self-Disclosure:

1. Models honesty and the altruism of self-disclosure needed for more cohesive interaction
2. Provides the therapeutic factors of universality and instillation of hope
3. Increases the level of trust between counselor and clients
4. Increases open communication
5. Provides the only person in the room who has actually been there and knows what it takes to overcome the problem
6. Provides information other professionals can learn from

Who wouldn't want to take advantage of all these most obvious and beneficial factors in treating those with addictions, especially when they are clearly supported for use in treating most any other psychological disturbance?

We must ask ourselves, why is it that so many treatment providers continue to discourage the use of self-disclosure? Do their explanations for this policy really outweigh the opinions of our experts? Could it just be a matter of protecting an agency's reputation of professionalism, given the degree of stigma in society. And if so, how ironic is that? How can some people profess to be against the stigma, while at the same time encourage it?

This practice of discouraging counselor self-disclosure is just another example of how professional practices stem from the beliefs of professionals in the field, beliefs that need to be addressed if treatment outcomes are ever going to improve. Like the experts, I am in no way suggesting a counselor self-disclose their story of incidents and experiences of using, as I think we can all understand the danger in this; but I also think we can clearly see the benefits of sharing the knowledge of previous addictions (appropriate disclosure), and what this openly free act of self-disclosure may mean for the person in treatment.

There is a video on YouTube called *The Power of Words*. In this video a blind man is sitting on a sidewalk with a sign that reads "I'm Blind, Please Help." Then it shows a few people walking right past him without tossing any money into his bucket. Soon a woman passes by and changes his sign to read, "It's a beautiful day, and I cannot see it." She hands the sign back to the blind man and goes on her merry way. Immediately afterward, everyone who passes by the blind man with his new sign stops to put a little something in his bucket. What a lesson to learn here.

This video was not so much about the power of words as it was about the *power of relating* – having gratitude for things taken for granted. Can it be that some addiction counselors take it for granted that they are not vulnerable to addiction? Or could it be that some believe they have the power to keep themselves from ever becoming addicted – like the addictions counselor I wrote about earlier? We can all relate to having a beautiful day and not being able to see it, but can we really relate to having an addiction and having no power over it? This is what recovered counselors can bring to the field, the power of relating. Let's welcome them with a sign that reads, "Free to Disclose – There is No Shame in Addiction Here."

This brings us to the conclusion of Part One. By now, I hope I have made it very clear that there exists a great need for change; that there is a clear division of causal beliefs within the profession, and that this division has a very negative impact on treatment outcomes; however, this makes perfectly good sense when we consider the fact that no singular piece of evidence can answer the all the mysterious and puzzling questions posed to it by addiction. There is no "addiction gene." It takes looking at all the little pieces of scientific fact and deducing what it all means when they are all put together. This means we cannot leave out even one piece of scientific evidence in reaching our collective conclusions. Such as, leaving out different degrees of effects or various levels of biological resistance to change. Each piece of evidence may answer only one piece of the puzzle, or it may take a few pieces of evidence to answer one question; such as looking to the evidence of genetic markers, replication errors (genetic mutations), epigenetics, and animal experiments to comprehend and answer the question of randomization in families where there is a history of addiction, compared to the randomization of addiction found in families where there is no history. So, please journey on with me as I will be bringing you more highly significant pieces evidence to take into consideration in Part Two.

This is exciting stuff! Let's get to it!

PART TWO

Moving Forward!

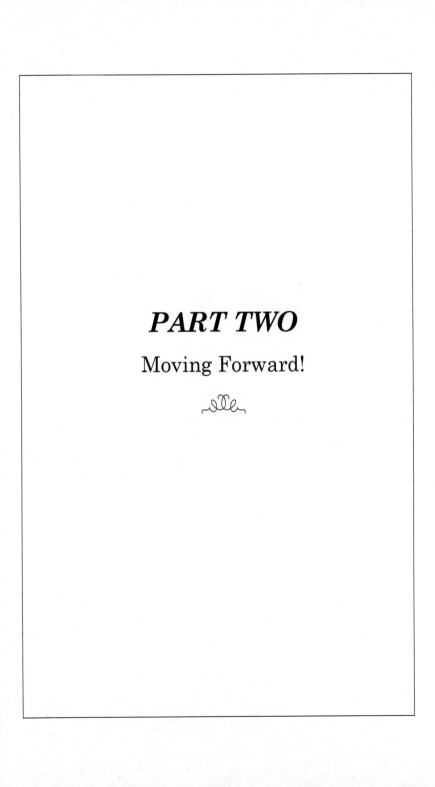

REVELATION –
"Something that is revealed....
A pleasant
often enlightening surprise"
– Merriam-Webster (2000)

Chapter 9

Moving Forward

Yes! We have finally made it to the heart of the book. Here we have a conceptualization of addiction that holds the potential to be much more effective than any conceptualization of the past. This is where the biological, psychological, and social aspects of addiction all come together like pieces of a puzzle to form an understanding of addiction that is very clear, plain, and simple.

First, this is all about those with addictions. I am not talking about the person who uses a substance on a fairly regular basis to cope with life or some other problematic issue. I am talking about those who experience very intense reactions to a chemical substance; those who are actually addicted; those who know what it is like to be a slave to a drug. Some of you may know exactly what it is I am talking about here; the intrinsic knowledge that only addicts may be privy to; the knowledge that there is more to a chemical addiction than just a mental obsession with using; the gut-wrenching need to quench a biological calling for the drug; the incessantly persistent and seemingly endless gnawing that lies far below any thought: an actual craving. At times, this craving may be hardly noticeable, and at others, it cannot be ignored. Again, and to be precisely clear, we are talking about addictions with biological, psychological, and social-environmental components – actual chemical addictions.

Part Two is about understanding how various circumstances and conditions can lead to chemical addictions. It is comprised of the evidence and facts that form the basis for the distinctions made between the psychosocial and biological causal perspectives presented in Part One, both of which are included in the Bio-Psycho-Social Model of Addiction. However, at this point it may be helpful to start thinking of the "Bio" part of this model as the *cause* of addiction and the Psycho and Social parts as *catalysts* (fuel). The concepts presented here, which is nothing more than taking a step back and looking at all the evidence, the big picture, allow us to see how the biological, psychosocial and social components all work together in the development of addiction. It is only through coming together on all the underlying aspects of addiction will we see any real improvements in treatment effectiveness.

What good is all the evidence and knowledge our scientists and researchers have gathered for us over the past few decades if we do not understand how to put this information to use? Where do we draw the lines between facts, theories, and interpretations? Let's start by highlighting some of the most important and salient features of **Addiction & Bio-Vulnerability**:

1. Addiction is a chemically induced mental illness.
2. Addiction is the result of biological, psychological, and social adaptations (factors).
3. Addiction is an incessant and abnormal desire-to-use that resides in the heart (emotion), mind (thought), and body (neurological "not-okay") of those afflicted.
4. Biological vulnerability consists of two parts: (1) the level or intensity of *effects*, and (2) various degrees of resistance to change, *neurological adaptations*.
5. Biological vulnerability can be identified as an idiosyncratic or unusually intense response to a psychotropic substance.
6. Addiction affects one's level of mental health through *psychological adaptations*, such as: impulsivity, cognitive decline, low self-esteem, and emotional instability.
7. Addiction affects one's mental health through *psychosocial adaptations*, such as: anti-social behaviors (lying, cheating, stealing), isolation, legal problems, conflicted relationships, and placing oneself at risk of abuse and trauma, etc.

And, most importantly:

8. *Addiction cannot occur without some degree of biological vulnerability, which is where all chemical addictions stem from; the actions of chemicals on the brain.*

These statements may seem a little presumptuous to some, rather like assuming the chicken came before the egg, but rest assured, they are based on the research and evidence we have available to us. One must possess a biological predisposition toward a specific drug in order for an addiction to develop. This is not easy to envision. It is much easier to fall into the trap of focusing on what appears to be very simple and logical explanations for addictive use, such as the desire to alter one's emotional state (either to avoid negative feelings or seek more positive feelings). However, when we delve too deeply into any one potential cause for use, we miss the big picture. Yes, it is the use of a drug that causes addiction; however, research consistently shows us that not all people are as vulnerable to the *effects* and/or *adaptations* from the use of various drugs as others.

This "big-picture" conceptualization holds the key to all the perplexing questions that have plagued scientists and addiction specialists for decades. All we have to do is pick up what has been laid at our feet and apply them without bias. This is much easier said than done. We may just have to do a little unlearning in order to make room for this new depth of knowledge. Why? The psychosocial causal perspective of chemical addictions does not work, or at least, it does not work well enough. In fact, there may even be a bit of an iatrogenic response occurring with such a one-sided focus on causation.

Iatrogenic means – treatment causing illness. This is what happens when attempts to cure an illness causes other problems or exacerbates an existing condition. With such low rates of first attempt recovery (<2%), this suspicion may not be so far-fetched. For example, back in the days that preceded the use of antiseptics, from the 1600s to the late 1800s, many newborns were infected by the dirty hands of their birthing physicians, a condition physicians referred to as childbed fever. (In addictions, we might call an iatrogenic reaction relapse.) This caused newborns to die shortly after birth. In the late 1800s Dr. Ignaz Semmelweis noticed that more children were dying from childbed fever in physician assisted births than in home births (at a ratio of nine to one!) and he concluded that since women were always washing their hands, the lack of hand washing was probably responsible for this. He conducted his own investigative study on the matter and when he published his findings he was publicly laughed at and ridiculed. Not having the knowledge of germs causing infections at the time, most all physicians refused to adopt hand washing into their practice. Part of this reaction was due to *disbelief*, but it was also due to the simple fact that they were doctors, and as such, they considered themselves to be "clean." They were the professionals in their field and they had been delivering babies ever since the beginning of the profession, and they were not about to change without *more conclusive evidence*, regardless of the cost. After all, they were the majority. Sound familiar? This is probably why they scoffed at the evidence Doctor Semmelweis provided; which for that time in history, was conducted very scientifically. As a result of this *widespread disbelief*, thousands of children continued to die at the hands of their physicians, literally, until the discovery of germs finally put an end to this madness, this professional stubbornness.

The comparison here is clear. The psychosocial approach of assuming that addictions stem from mental difficulties, using lifestyles, or poor coping skills may be what leads people further and further into their addictions. We will know the truth only after the biological perspective becomes widely accepted (like the reality of germs) and applied; when we begin to see improvements in treatment effectiveness as a result. Obviously, some well-designed treatment experiments could be performed, but this would take some highly trained therapists who were also thoroughly committed to the biological perspective, which may be hard, if not impossible to find at this early stage of implementation. Such studies would also have to be conducted on a large scale basis and implemented in multiple facilities across several states to provide the kind of results significant enough to impact and question the beliefs of the majority: those of the psychosocial perspective.

By the way, Dr. Ignaz Semmelweis, the physician who attempted to warn other physicians of contamination through unclean hands, was so scorned and rejected by the medical community that he was eventually committed to a mental asylum where he remained until his death. How pitiful was that? It is not easy to stand up against the majority, but sometimes you just have to do what you know in your heart to be right. The difference here is that today we do have the evidence; however it is being selectively misapplied, and for the most part just outright ignored, all because of personal bias and previously held beliefs.

In the following chapters we will look at some practical examples of how to apply this understanding in treatment, but first, let's take a look at some basic facts. We have considered quite a bit of evidence already, such as: the identical twin studies of the midcentury; the student study with the use of biological knowledge in reducing college consumption rates; differences in the number of dopamine (D2) receptors accounting for different effects (Dr. Nora Volkow); alcohol producing stimulant effects only in alcoholics; the genes associated with nicotine addiction having been identified; genes identified for having a high tolerance to alcohol. However, these are not necessarily facts. It is this type of evidence facts are derived from. All facts are based on some form of tangible evidence, such as objective observances and experience. In the conceptualization of chemical addictions the three most important facts to be consistently and consciously aware of are:

1. Drugs cause addiction – for without them, addiction is not even possible.
2. Chemicals produce different degrees of *effects* (intensity) in different people
3. Chemicals produce different degrees of *neurological adaptation* (based on varying levels of bio-resistance)

We will refer back to how these three facts play out in the conceptualization of addiction, but first, let's take a look at more evidence that support these facts. First, let's consider the fact that humans are nearly identical to monkeys in terms of genetic similarities. Our genetic comparisons are measured to be between 97% for Rhesus monkeys (this is where our R- and R+ blood types were found) and as high as 98.9% for Chimpanzees. This means that conducting chemical experiments on monkeys can be very important and insightful.

In a 1972 experiment at least one monkey was found to avoid social contact with other monkeys and consume cocaine until death when given the freedom to self-administer. (For those concerned, as I am, I was told this experiment was stopped once the first monkey died.) Of significant importance here, is that this provided clear evidence that it was the *effects* of cocaine (the drug) on this particular monkey that propelled him to this extreme. This is a prime example of how different levels of biological predisposition exist in monkeys. We know this because some more recent studies have also observed different reactions, such as not touching the cocaine again after trying it or maintaining food consumption while using. This really shows how much of an *effect* (not adaptation) cocaine can have on only *some* monkeys, but not all of them. Evidence like this is hard to negate. As humans we have the ability to think about our thinking and the consequences of our actions, which really distinguishes us as being superior to all animals in the realm of mental ability. However, we may never really know how much of a role mental abilities can play in overriding the effects of various chemicals on various brains. *This is why we can state with a clear conscience that drugs cause addiction, not just the use of them.* This is because not everyone who tries a drug receives the same exact effects.

Recently, there was another experiment with monkeys being conducted in Oregon. This one was about observing the different effects and responses to alcohol among monkeys when given the freedom of choice. As reported, this study also supports varying *degrees* of biological vulnerability. What is most interesting about this study is that the percentages of no-use, moderate-use, misuse, and excessive-use parallel that of human consumption. About 7-15% do not drink at all, some drink very little; others drink on a fairly consistent basis, some drink to drunkenness but not every day; and about another 7-15% drink every day and appear to be fairly well addicted.

It also showed differences in tolerance. They had one monkey called Mohawk who consumed quite a bit more than the others and even pushed the other monkeys away from the tap in order to protect his supply. He did not get as drunk as the others who consume equal or lesser amounts, which indicated a higher level of tolerance. This experiment confirmed for us the clear existence of biological differences in animals; and since humans are also animals, this puts the psychosocial perspective of causation into serious question (Monkey, 2011). This does not mean psychosocial factors do not play a significant role in the *development* of addictions; it just reinforces the fact that biological factors play a much greater role in the *causation* of addiction than has ever been acknowledged or accepted.

Other extremely relevant studies involve the observation of significant behavioral changes in experiments with monkeys. According to Erik Schiorring (1977), "In various animal species it has been found consistently that all mammalian species respond to the administration of amphetamine and related compounds with marked changes in individual and social behaviors (various stereotypes and social withdrawal).... It is our opinion... that CNS-stimulants (including cocaine) produce profound pathological conditions" (Ellinwood & Kilbey, 1977, pp. 481-482). In the book *Ecstasy*, it is written, "Observers of operant behavior of primates have reported interference with grooming and social interactions and the loss of conditioned behavior due to MDMA..." (Peroutka, 1990, p.10). Although I am only referencing a few drugs here, all psychotropic drugs have a profound effect on the psyche and thus, one's behavior. From this, I believe it is clear to see how drugs are actually the culprit in producing all the common psychological disturbances found in addicts, not the other way around. As you can see from the dates above, this significantly relevant evidence is hardly anything new. It has however, not been taken very seriously.

There have also been studies conducted with rats that support varying degrees of *effect*. These experiments replicated the effects of heroin in humans. We still do not know why a specific amount of heroin can be consumed on one day, and on another the same amount or less can cause death, but the rat experiment produced these same mysterious results. This experiment also provided evidence that some rats were much more affected by heroin than others, as some died off quicker than others. In this study, the same amounts of consumption produced different degrees of *effect*.

In regard to biological heredity, a fruit fly experiment was conducted. Here, researchers found that after 25 generations (about 3 months) of exposing fruit flies to alcohol vapors, only a percentage of the last generation of fruit flies were genetically altered (only some of them adapted to the exposure of alcohol with the passing down of an increase in tolerance to their offspring). This is highly significant. At the beginning of the experiment, nearly all the fruit flies were falling off their perch when alcohol vapors were first introduced; however, after 25 generations of exposure, only about half of the fruit flies were falling off their perch. This indicated that only about 50% of the fruit flies were genetically altered, leaving the other 50% unaffected. This is interesting because it provides a factual understanding of why only some children of addicts are likely to become addicts while others do not. It also puts our psychosocial explanations for this phenomenon into question as well. Epigenetics can also help to explain this randomization, and may even provide a better understanding of why this happens.

These animal experiments all support the absolute reality that biological differences in response to various drugs do indeed exist. Biological differences in mental abilities are not involved here, so these studies really help to demonstrate that the lack of mental ability has nothing to do with biological predisposition. Supporters of the psychosocial perspective would have you believing that biological vulnerability, of the biopsychosocial model, is a reference to genetically impaired mental abilities rather than to actual differences in biological *reactions*. I have seen this misinterpretation and misapplication of biological vulnerability in the field, and I suspect it may have grown out of a need for some providers to fit the bio aspect of the Biopsychosocial Model of Addiction into their own understanding, which is clearly meant to put the cause of addiction right back on the psychological tract.

All too often biological differences are ignored and replaced by what appears to be more logical explanations for using. These include: attachment issues, psychological distress, childhood and adult traumas, peer influences, emotional immaturity, emotional pain and suffering, poor choices, lack of control, using attitudes, poverty, depression, starting to use at an early age, boredom, etc. It is very clear that all these factors contribute to the *development* of chemical addictions; however, they cannot *cause* addiction in and of themselves.

In fact, these factors can only contribute to the development of addiction in those who are biologically vulnerable.

They represent the progression of the disease and become more salient as the *desire-to-use* (addiction) becomes more severe, which is a result of biopsychosocial adaptations. This is why it is very important to keep the facts of addiction at the forefront of any perception one may hold, especially when making any reference or inference to causation.

FACTS OF ADDICTION

1. Addiction is an intense *desire* and *obsession* to use a chemical substance
2. Cessation (stopping) of use alone does not resolve an addiction (the desire-to-use)
3. Psychoactive & psychotropic chemicals affect people differently (effects & adaptations)
4. Some people are immune to some addictions due to adverse effects (negative reactions)
5. Addiction can only occur in people who receive a benefit from use (positive reactions)
6. Stronger drugs create higher risks for addiction (e.g. alcohol vs. heroin)
7. The use of a psychotropic drug does not cause addiction in most people
8. Addiction is dependent upon the amount of use in relation to individual *degrees* of biopsychosocial vulnerabilities
9. Intensities of effect and resistance to neurological change vary among people
10. The impact of chemicals on the brain are not factors in non-chemical addictions

Some of these facts are often overlooked or ignored in the field of addiction. For example, it is important to remember that many people over-drink and over-indulge in the use of chemicals during times of loss or stress, such as the loss of a loved one, the loss of a job, or during a separation or divorce, as well as on special occasions without becoming addicted. This response to loss or stress is considered to be rather normal in most societies. There are a couple of points that need to be highlighted here; (1) addicts as well as non-addicts respond this way; and, (2) these factors do not, in and of themselves, cause addiction. They can only contribute to addiction for those who are biologically vulnerable.

An increase in use from stress, loss, or celebration can contribute to sending some people over the edge, from a perceived sense of control over their use, to an actual loss-of-control, but only for those who are already prone to addiction – not most people. I have seen this over and over again. This reaction to psycho-emotional stress may give the impression that psycho-social issues alone cause addiction; however, this "going-over-the-edge" reaction is really just a part of the progression (for the brain has already been altered). For most addicts, it doesn't take anything as drastic as losing a loved one to send them over the edge, the mere ups and downs of everyday life can be more than enough to do the trick.

Clearly, addiction is the result of a combination of biological predisposition, psycho-emotional ills, and social-environmental influences; however, as we discovered in Part One, too many professionals focus primarily on the psychological and social aspects alone. As a result, they inadvertently or subtly imply, if not outright proclaim, that psychological and emotional problems *cause* addiction. This presumption creates an enormous barrier to recovery for those with addictions who have *not yet* progressed to devastating levels of despair and hopelessness.

The assumption that poor psychological and emotional health <u>causes</u> addiction puts clients on the defensive; they cannot help but to resist such an attack upon their character and prove to themselves, and others, that they are not lacking in psychological abilities, especially for those who have accomplished some degree of success in their lives; such as teachers, policemen, politicians, actors, musicians, business men, nurses, physicians, etc.

There is no doubt the accusation of personal responsibility in *causing* one's own addiction, regardless of how subtly implied or presented, becomes a huge barrier to recovery. This is what most addicts resist with all they have. An attempt to help, in illuminating this so-called reality of self-responsible causation, actually feeds the progression of addiction. This is why it is paramount that addicts become aware of the fact that they could not become addicted to any substance without having a biological susceptibility to the effects of the substance in the first place. This is where all chemical addictions begin. They do not begin in poor child-rearing or any such childhood travesty. If this were the case, every poorly raised child would be an addict, and this we know is not the case. Just like the example of childbed fever (infection), the simplest of explanations are often the hardest ones to see and accept.

This is a good time to mention that addicts do not have a "drug of *choice*." The use of this phrase is another prime example of how underlying beliefs continue to impact the field of addiction and influence public perception. This is the phrase commonly used to identify the drug a person is addicted to, their primary *drug of use*, or their *drug of addiction*. It is just another way well intentioned professionals go about insinuating that addicts *choose* their drug, and thus, implies that they *chose* to cause their own addiction. This has become such a commonly used phrase in the field of addiction that I am quite sure many treatment providers, and especially those new to the field, do not even notice the proclamation they are making when they use it. When one asks an addict what their drug of choice is, they are actually asking which drug the addict chose to become addicted to. This is actually a statement within a question. It is just like asking a mental health patient if they are happy with the life they have created. The question in this example is, "Are you happy with your life?" The underlying statement here, or proclamation being made, is, "You have created your life." Likewise, in the question, "What is your drug of choice? The question is, "What is the drug you are addicted to? The proclamation being made within this question here is, "You chose this drug" – Thus, the implied sediment within this one is, "You did it to yourself." This is an accusation. It condemns the addict for their using behavior, and they hear this all the time.

These little – seemingly harmless – subtleties speak much louder than words, for they are taken to heart at an unconscious level, which make them very powerful. It is simple little statements and gestures like this one that lead addicts into believing that they did this to themselves; that they created their own addiction. And, when they internalize such beliefs they become core beliefs, which are very hard to challenge and change (for the addict, as well as the provider). Therefore, we need to put a stop to these types of unfounded proclamations.

This inappropriate use of the word *choice* leads into a hierarchy of psychological superiority over addicts; this can also create a huge chasm between the counselor and client. Most counselors and most people for that matter, actually believe they possess the psychological ability and fortitude to keep themselves from ever becoming an addict. This becomes exceptionally evident when well-intentioned counselors, in a sincere and honest attempt to express genuine empathy and concern, say something like, "I would have been an addict too, if I had been through all that you have." This seemingly harmless, empathetic and compassionate remark is really telling the truth about how a counselor perceives addiction: <u>First</u>, it says your problems *caused* you to become an addict. <u>Secondly</u>, it proclaims you *chose* to turn to the use of drugs to cope with your problems (even though the counselor is not blaming you for this choice under your particular circumstances). <u>Thirdly</u>, it screams that being an addict is a character weakness, because you did not control it (feeding the stigma). And <u>lastly</u>, it shouts out to the addict that addiction is not a condition like any other biological condition, such as cancer, diabetes, heart disease, etc., which is likely to contradict what they may have been taught in the educational part of their treatment. This leads to plenty of confusion, and although the patient may not be consciously aware of these contradictions, it still creates a lot of confusion for them, especially when they try to incorporate other explanations. All they are likely to conclude is that *something does not make sense*. They may not be consciously aware of what it is, but it will be there just the same, and this will lead them down a very long and painful road to recovery.

As you may recall, we started this chapter with the three most important facts to know, important because they provide the basis for a sound understanding of addiction. Again, these three facts are: (1) Drugs cause addiction – for without them, drug addiction is not even possible; (2) Chemicals produce different degrees of *effects* (intensity); and, (3) Chemicals produce different degrees of *neurological adaptation* (based on varying degrees of biological resistance to change).

These are not theory, they are the facts that evidence has provided us. So, how do we go about applying these facts? First, I suggest we have to accept them. This is the hard part. We cannot continue to go on with what it is we want to believe or what we think makes the most sense to each and every one of us any longer. This is where we have been for far too long. For years and years we have been educating counselors on all the potential and possible causes of addiction and letting them decide for themselves which theories to apply, usually on a person-to-person individual basis. However, this approach has not improved treatment outcomes at all. I do agree that we need to treat each patient individually by addressing the specifics of each addict's personal reasons for using. However, it is a big mistake to insinuate that these issues are the only "cause" of the patient's addiction. This is why a universal conceptualization of addiction is so very important. We must teach others how to take all the information we have about chemical addictions and put them all together into an acceptable and useful format. We must show them how all the pieces of the puzzle fit together into a more complete and comprehensive picture. We can no longer leave it up to individual beliefs; we have far too much evidence for that.

As I have stated, some much acknowledged researchers, such as Dr. Nora Volkow from NIDA, have concluded that biological vulnerabilities [effects and adaptations] may be responsible for 40-60% of one's addiction. Therefore, psycho-social factors play a role in the development of chemical addictions as well. However, this is where it gets a little tricky, conceptualizing how the three most important facts play out. For example, (1) Take a trauma victim with no propensity for drug use, thus, having no bio-vulnerability, and they will never develop an addiction. (2) Take a trauma victim with a propensity for drug use and a moderate level of bio-vulnerability, and developing an addiction is more probable, but not inevitable. (3) Add in an intense reaction to a substance with a low level of resistance to neurological adaptation, therefore, having a very high level of bio-vulnerability, and now the probability is highly likely and may even be inevitable without some type of intervention. This is because all people experience trauma to one degree or another and most trauma victims never develop chemical addictions. Biological vulnerability, one's individual reaction and response to a specific substance, is the only common link.

So, what does this tell us? (1) One must have a propensity for drug use (initial effects), and (2) one must be vulnerable to neurological adaptation. People do NOT *need* any type of mental deficiency of psychological disturbance for an addiction to develop (as no single disturbance or deficiency has ever been found). They do, however, *need* some degree of biological vulnerability (effects and adaptation). Even poor mental health cannot lead to addiction without it. This is why we can tell patients that their addiction was not caused by any external factors, such as one's mama, papa, traumas, etc., even though they most likely played a role in the person's quantity and frequency of use in the progression of the addiction. You could call these other factors, such as various traumas and mental impairments, partial causes or catalysts but they are certainly not the root cause. This is what we all need to learn and understand: *the root or foundational cause of addiction is all biological.* Whether or not a person develops an addiction to a specific substance is basically just the luck of the draw, not only to biological vulnerability, but to all the psychological and social-environmental vulnerabilities as well; such as in the case of trauma contributing to the addiction. So, if one is biologically susceptible, such as experiencing very intense initial effects, they would probably be drawn into addiction on biology alone. Add in some mental health issues and some stress, and they don't stand a chance of avoiding it. This is why we can tell our patients, with complete confidence and a clear conscience that their addiction was not of their own making – not their fault – not even partially! This is the knowledge addicts need in order to take on the responsibility of having to address their addiction. This is where the matter of choice comes in.

Choosing to address an addiction and choosing whether or not to use in active addiction are two entirely different things.

All too often the distinction between these two choices gets muddled and confused in treatment with the thinking that "to choose not to use" is the same thing as "choosing to address addiction." I can assure you they are not; this is where most addicts have been failed in treatment. If addicts are not taught what addiction is (the intense and persistent desire-to-use), and become convinced that they have an addiction (acceptance), there is no possible way for them to choose whether or not to address it. All addicts can stop using for short periods of time, but unless they know *why* they must stop for good, they cannot stay stopped. This is the condition itself. The drive to use will always prevail; that is, unless they are given all the evidence, not just pictures of damaged brains. They must be shown that their *choice* to use was stolen from them by their biological reaction to the drug (effects and adaptations), to which they have also developed psychosocial dependencies that need to be addressed and overcome.

The point here is that unless we provide addicts with all our evidence – and WHAT THIS EVIDENCE MEANS – they can hardly make a well-informed decision for themselves; they cannot choose to address their addiction if they do not know what it is they are choosing. As it stands, under the psycho-social perspective, we continue to lead them to great depths of despair with an insistence on self-causation. Not only does this not work very well, it is no longer acceptable. We have too much evidence to the contrary.

We must remember, that for the addicted, choosing never to use again is never going to be their first choice; the addiction is in the way. All they really want is a way to use without having to suffer the consequences. This means they want to be able to use like normal people; they want to be able to control their use. To the addict, using and being normal are one in the same. This is what society has taught them and this is *why* they must know about their biological difference. It is the very reason why they must stop using for good and why they cannot use like other people; they are, in fact, *different* in regards to their biological reaction to the drug.

This is the information we can take forward into the 21st century, and I, for one, am very excited about it. I have no doubts about the value and effectiveness of genetic predisposition, but we may need a little more understanding if we are going to make the best possible use of it. We will need to explore the intrinsic interaction between the biological, psychological and social factors, and how this interaction plays out in the development and progression of chemical addictions.

REPERCUSSION –
"A widespread, indirect,
or <u>unforeseen effect</u> of an
act, action, or event"
– Merriam-Webster (2000)

Chapter 10

Genetic Predisposition

Is addiction the result of biological, psychological, and social reactions and responses to the effects of a drug, or is it the result of willful indulgence and the inability to cope effectively with life's challenges? If we accept all the evidence and facts we have before us, we can only reach one conclusion: *Addiction is the result of one's bio/psycho/social reaction to drugs.* Addiction is not within the control of one's mind or will. The only way to prevent or control addiction, for those who are highly vulnerable to the overpowering effects of a drug is to refrain from use altogether – complete abstinence. The only way we can identify and address addictions early-on is to acknowledge the changes we see in those who experience different or intense biological reactions. All we really need do is just acknowledge these differences: the effect drugs can have on one's *use* (loss-of-control), *thinking* (protection of use), *feelings* (numb/ altered), and *be-*

havior (self-pleasing). This may be a rather crude and broad observation, but this is what the drug produces in those who are highly susceptible to a drug's effects. Why do you think the monkey Mohawk guarded his supply? The occurrence of these behavior changes do not happen on their own. They are responses to the effects of drugs on the brain. In those who are vulnerable, the drug changes how people think and act.

When it comes to adolescents who are using, all too often we blame their use on "bad" behavior. We neglect to see the bad behavior as a result of their induction into drug use. This does not happen to all teenagers who try a drug. It happens to those who are more impacted by a drug than others, those who are vulnerable to the drug's effects. Shortly after initiation, they experience a change in interests, attitudes, and behaviors. All too often, these changes go unnoticed until these kids experience consequences for their bad behaviors. Then other repercussions fuel more use and the long spiral of progression begins. Sadly, many of the hardships, trials, and traumas these children experience would not have happened if they were not exposed to and impacted by the drug in the first place. What is worse, these children cannot make the connection between all the terrible things they are experiencing in life (after the initiation of drug use) with the use of their drug. They are likely to go on using for many years blaming their use on the troubles they are experiencing in life, totally unaware that most of their troubles are a direct result of their using. The worst thing one can do is to feed into all these excuses for addiction with inappropriate empathetic responses; such as, "If I had been through all that you have, I'd have been an addict too." They must be made aware that their troubles in life did not cause them to become an addict, the drug did. This is the bottom line.

Most people believe they can control their amount of consumption; and, in doing so, they can prevent themselves from becoming an addict. The ironic part is, most addicts believed this at one time or another, too. This is why so many people believe that addiction is the result of a series of "bad" choices to use and the inability to cope effectively with various challenges in life (e.g., childhood abuse, sexual abuse, stress, using parents, mental health issues, etc.). This is the fallacy that leads to the blaming we have been talking about. It is this way of thinking that teaches addicts to either blame themselves or others, and this is a major barrier to recovery. As most people know, resentments are the number one cause of relapse, and it does not matter if the resentment is against someone else or themselves. And, most importantly, it is this perspective that prevents addicts from accepting their condition. This is a huge barrier because it requires that the addict accept responsibility for playing a part in "causing" their addiction.

In reality, the non-vulnerable person can no more make themselves an addict than a highly vulnerable person can prevent it.

Without knowledge, and more importantly, the acceptance of it, millions of people will continue to be sucked into the grips of addiction before they even know what hit them. This is why addiction is so baffling, cunning, and powerful – it strikes normal people, just like you and me, every day of the year, day in and day out.

The plain fact is just this: For those who have an intense reaction and response to a chemical substance – those with a genetic predisposition – addiction is just as probable as one's ability to keep on using, which is solely dependent upon opportunity and availability. Quantity and frequency of use causes addiction in those who are vulnerable to the effects and adaptations of drug use, and this varies among the population. External factors, such as those that come from personal responsibilities (e.g., spouse, children, work, etc.), and even bouts of self-loathing may slow the progression down a little because they reduce the amount of quantity and frequency of use, but these external factors will not stop it. This susceptibility is beyond human control; it is a reaction and response to a drug, period. It is this biological reaction to a drug that will never change and will only get worse with continued use.

What is important to understand here is that it is the biological response to the drug in question, that the addict is born with, is what cannot be changed. This is genetic predisposition. This is what causes addiction in the first place and why one's biological reaction to a substance is permanent. It is permanent because it has always been there – remaining behind the scenes and unnoticed (causing neurological structures of the brain to slowly adapt and change with continual use) until an addiction develops and takes hold. It is through this slow adaptation of brain structures that addiction develops and becomes visible.

Therefore, it IS the biological causal aspects of addiction (effects and vulnerability to neurological change) that are <u>permanent</u> – NOT the result of this change (biopsychosocial adaptations).

All the biological, psychological and sociological adaptations that occur with addiction can be addressed and overcome. Even the brain is pliable, which means this too can heal in time; such as in the evidence of dopamine levels eventually returning to normal in the lab mice experiment (Kuhar, 2012). It is like an allergic reaction to strawberries, where the person who is allergic breaks out in a rash, but with abstinence the rash eventually heals. This is how it is with addiction. In this analogy, the *addiction*, the desire-to-use, is the rash that will heal in time with abstinence, and the *vulnerability* to bio-adaptation, is the allergic reaction that is permanent. This is what makes it possible for addicts to fully recover. They will always carry the vulnerability (the allergic reaction) with them, but that does not mean that they will always carry the addiction, the desire-to-use – the rash.

In chemical addictions, the biological part of the desire-to-use, the *cravings* (the rash), will dissipate in time with complete abstinence. Abstinence will alleviate biological cravings. However, abstinence will not alleviate all the psychological and social-environmental aspects of the desire-to-use, these *obsessions* and *longings* that are bound to remain. Psychosocial adaptations need to be addressed separately through therapeutic interventions. *If they are not, they can activate biological cravings.* Brain imaging studies have proven this. Even after three months of abstinence, parts of the limbic system (seen in brain imaging) light up when addicts are shown millisecond pictures of drugs and using paraphernalia. This is why recovery takes so long and cannot be addressed through abstinence alone.

It is believing in and the accepting one's biological reaction to a specific drug that make it possible for one to fully recover, instead of just being *in-recovery* forever. This term, in-recovery, clearly implies one is *not well*. One can come up with a million and one explanations for why this term has been so widely accepted and used today, but there is no getting around the plain fact that the term *in-recovery* means to be *in a state of healing* – that one is not well. It undoubtedly originated from a misconception about what addiction is – believing that the *addiction* is permanent (not just the *vulnerability* to addiction, which is the actual case), and therefore, resulting in the belief that one must maintain their mental and spiritual well-being in order to remain sober. This may work well for those addicts who buy into the *belief* that there is something mentally or spiritually wrong with them, and that they probably did cause their own addiction, but this is far from what we are learning. According to the evidence, addicts are sucked into their addiction by their biological *reaction* to the substance they are vulnerable to. It is that simple.

In order to clear up the misconception of addictions being permanent (and thus, requiring a lifelong recovery program) we first have to know what an addiction is and be able to define it. We need to know the difference between symptoms and the cause of those symptoms. We need to know what is permanent and what is not.

For example, take a person with the chronic condition of joint pain (symptom) from celiac disease (CD), which is a gene related autoimmune disorder. Gluten-containing foods exacerbate the inflammation that causes the joint pain. So, if people with CD avoid gluten, and their joint pain disappears, do they need a recovery program to stay away from gluten? Obviously not, but that does not mean that they do not have a permanent genetic susceptibility to gluten, which they will probably always have. Therefore, in this analogy the person has who has fully recovered from their joint pain, still carry a genetic predisposition to gluten. It is the same for addiction.

So, what are the specific genes, or sets of genes, that make some people more susceptible to addiction than others? Well, this is still a work in progress and there is a great effort being put into identifying them. However, at this point we are pretty sure there is no single gene responsible for addiction; rather, the cause is being identified in groups of genes for various chemicals. Wim van den Brink, Professor of Psychiatry and Addiction at the University of Amsterdam, informs us of twelve genes that are highly suspect to playing a role in the development of alcoholism. These have been identified as: OPRM1, DRD1, COMT, GRIN2B, GABRA6, DRD2, SERT, MAOA, CNR1, HTR1B, GABRB2, and GABRG2 (Psychiatry Research, 2015 http://progressinmind.elsevierresource.com). This is another video I highly recommend and the complete link can be found in the References section.

These genes may not mean much of anything to most of us, but the fact that they are being identified is huge. Having some or all of these genes is what makes some people more susceptible to alcoholism than those with fewer or none of them. This set was found to be significantly accurate when tested against three patient populations on two continents, in two ethnicities, and in both genders. In mouse studies, Dr. Alexander Niculesscu reports that 66 variations of these genes, called single-nucleotide polymorphisms, have also been identified (IUSM, 2014). This helps us to understand the vastly diverse potential for a wide range of vulnerability in biological predisposition. That within bio-vulnerability, the range can extend from being slightly vulnerable to highly vulnerable depending on how many of these genes (and/or variations of them) one may possess.

This knowledge is of great importance when it comes to understanding addiction because it helps to explain some of our unanswered questions. When it comes to genetics, identical twins studies confirm how strongly genetics play a role, but they are not absolute. For example, if biology is at the root of all chemical addictions, then how is it that one identical twin of those separated at birth develop an addiction when their identical twin does not? Well, when we understand that biological vulnerability exists on a continuum, we can begin to understand that when identical twins have none of these genes, neither twin will develop alcoholism. And, when they share a lot of these genes, both will develop alcoholism, and this happens despite being raised in different environments. This leads us to conclude that when identical twins are only somewhat vulnerable, meaning they only share a few of these genes (and thus, they can go either way), the amount of alcohol each one of these twins consume would be the determining factor (as in the fact; drugs cause addiction), and this is when social-environmental factors come into play. However, don't be misled into thinking psychosocial factors are causing alcoholism in this situation. The cause is still the biological reaction to alcohol. With no genetic predisposition, there is no addiction. In the words of Dr. Stuart Gitlow, the president of the American Society of Addiction Medicine (ASAM), "I can't turn someone who isn't alcoholic into an alcoholic by giving them alcohol" (Commentary, 2013). This explains why there is such a high correlation for both identical twins to be either alcoholic or non-alcoholic despite vastly different life experiences, and why only some identical twins become alcoholic when their twin doesn't. It all depends on how much biological vulnerability exists in their shared set of genes.

This concept of multiple genes applies to other drugs as well, such as gene sets that have been identified for opiate, cocaine, and nicotine addictions. It also tells us that biological vulnerability exists on a continuum – on a scale from least susceptible to most susceptible. Therefore, one's individual level or degree of bio-vulnerability rests in the genes one is born with and can be different for various substances. It explains why one person can be highly susceptible to alcohol, another to nicotine, and another to cocaine, heroin, cannabis, etc.; why one can be vulnerable to one drug and detest another; or, why some can be vulnerable to only one or several of them.

Genetic predisposition provides answers to all the mysteries we have about chemical addictions. It answers why most people with mental health problems never become addicts. It explains why countries with higher rates of alcohol consumption have higher rates of alcoholism. It explains why some people go into alcoholic seizures at the age of 16, while others do not reach this level of adaptation until they are 45 or older, if ever. It also explains why some people experience loss-of-control (of their consumption) right from the start of their first use and why others develop this type of loss-of-control over time. It explains why most children raised in foreign countries, where the drinking of wine at the dinner table is the norm, never become alcoholics. It explains why most people who have experienced childhood abuse and other traumas in their life never become addicts. It explains why most people who abuse alcohol and other drugs never become addicts (adolescents and young adults, college students, etc.). When we acknowledge the biological differences in people all this starts to make perfectly good sense.

As for the concept of using at a young age, when the brain is in its developmental stage of growth, as *causing addiction*, this might only be an *assumption* because this is what we see. It only makes sense that drugs would cause more damage on these underdeveloped brains, and evidence supports this. However, we must also take into consideration the actual cause of addiction. If addiction was caused by frontal lobe deficiencies, responsible for high impulsivity and poor decision making skills, then this would make sense. However, if addiction is caused by the drug's impact on the inner core structures of the brain, in the mesolimbic region, which may be fully developed by childhood, and not by deficiencies in the frontal cortex, then only the children with a genetic predisposition to a substance would be the ones using. Many children experiment with drugs at an early age, but not all of them continue using on a regular basis unless they are attracted to the effects and genetically vulnerable to the substance they are trying.

I am in no way disputing the evidence we have in regards to the damage drugs can do to the underdeveloped brains of children, for the evidence we have is pretty sound. Drug use by children results in lower brain mass and the problems associated with lower brain mass include poor impulse control and poor problem solving abilities. I am not disputing any evi-

dence we have. In fact, I am using all of it. What I am disputing is the assumption (taken from this evidence) that "using at
an early age causes addiction" – that addiction is the result of
lower brain mass, high impulsivity, and poor decision making
skills. In fact, it is probably the other way around. What we do
know is that people with addictions exhibit all these problems,
whether they started using at the age of ten or at the age of
thirty.

In other words, the frontal lobe deficiencies we find in
adults with addictions (who started using as children) may not
have anything at all to do with causation. This may be a hard
concept to understand, but since nearly 80% of all children
experiment with some form of drug, and most of them never
develop an addiction later in life, we need to question the interpretation of these findings. Again, this is likely to be another
example of how the psychosocial perspective is infecting or
swaying how we interpret the evidence we do have.

Put more simply, it is very likely that we will see deficits in
cognitive functions in children more prone to drug use, because
of their individual reactions to the drug. Once a substance is
tried, this will determine which kids will be the ones continuing to use (and thus, doing damage to their brains) and which
ones will not. In addition, this evidence of drugs doing harm
to underdeveloped brains is no different than the evidence
compiled in our so-called risk-factors for addiction, which we
already covered in a previous chapter. We cannot take evidence
from only those known to have an addiction and apply it to
everyone. Addiction does not lie in the frontal cortex, it lies
much farther down in the core structures of the brain, in the

limbic region. This is what brain imaging studies have confirmed. Certainly, frontal cortex health can help to thwart off or slow down the progression of addiction, but it is unlikely to stop it, especially for those who are highly vulnerable.

Regardless of peer pressure, we will not see children, or even young adults for that matter, using if they have a slight or adverse reaction to a substance/drug; and, it is foolish to assume that those who try drugs and do not continue with the use of them to be in any way better developed than those who react to them. This reaction has nothing to do with mental and emotional health, or coming from a closer knit family or having a better upbringing. To think otherwise may just be the influence of the psychosocial perspective and our own natural human fear of not having complete control over our behavior.

The psychosocial perspective of causation certainly applies to the *initiation* of use, but after that, it is all biological. It is the biological reaction that will ultimately determine who will and will not develop an addiction. All it may take is one episode of use to set the wheels of addiction in motion. Children with more biological vulnerability will be more likely to continue using despite any degree of consequence. This does not mean they are behaving "badly," they are merely doing what comes natural to them. For some, it is like setting a fish to water. Likewise, those who refrain from using are not being "good," they are merely responding to less intense or adverse effects from the drug. This is why some will show a degree of control or restraint despite peer pressure. We must remember the one fact we know for sure – *drugs can only cause addiction in those who are biologically vulnerable.* It may take years for an addiction to fully develop, but if we were to see signs of loss-of-control, either in frequency or amount of consumption, this would indicate a genetic predisposition. This is how we can use the biological perspective to intervene much sooner, at an earlier age, and implement better prevention strategies. Soon we will be able to test children who are suspect to having a genetic predisposition; and the results could be used for motivational enhancement, but for now all we have are the observable symptoms. However, through the acceptance of genetic predisposition, we can initiate better preventions strategies now.

Those who are not very vulnerable to a drug's effects are unlikely to experience a loss-of-control over their use. Whereas, those more vulnerable are much more likely to have this symptom. Loss-of-control is how we can identify those who are truly at risk and challenge them to address their condition instead of telling them to just say no. We know how well this works! Let me reiterate, biological vulnerability is not a dichotomy (have or have not), it exists in levels or degrees of vulnerability. This is easier to understand on a continuum from adverse or minimal *effects* at one end of scale to extremely pleasurable effects at the other. It also includes degrees, or levels of resistance to change, the various levels of vulnerability to *bio-adaptations* that vary from one person to the next, but cannot be seen.

Those who experience highly intense effects from a drug would be considered to have a high genetic predisposition. Likewise, those who are born with a high tolerance to a substance (as some gene-sets have already been identified) would also be considered to have a genetic predisposition. Exactly how much of a genetic predisposition to a specific substance, without being able to see or measure levels of neurological adaptation, would be hard to impossible to determine at this point in time; however, we do know they exist along a continuum from low to high as well. We also know that it is these neurological adaptations that are responsible for the real biological cravings addicts suffer from. So, if what we observe appears to be coming from an uncontrollable biological source, cravings, and not just a lust or obsession to use, we can be pretty sure this person is genetically predisposed.

The following diagram depicts alcohol consumption along a continuum and is representative of genetic predisposition. This concept of viewing vulnerability along a continuum, instead of black or white, using versus not using, addicted or not addicted, is a concept we will need to understand if we are going to gain a thorough understanding of genetic predisposition.

BIOLOGIC CONTINUUM OF VULNERABILITY

←dislikes/negatively impacted - - - - - to - - - - - highly impacted/loves →

No Use	Limited Use	Heavy Use	Abuse/Addicted
15%	40%	30%	15%

45% at-risk of alcoholism

This continuum is a representation of individual reactions to the use of various drugs and reflects the known statistical figures we have on the percentages of alcohol use and addiction. Seven to 15% of the population is addicted to some form of psychotropic substance. This has been about the same for as long as we have been keeping records; approximately 45 to 50 percent of the U.S. population drinks rather heavily, and according to some researchers are at risk for addiction; about another 40 percent drink very moderately with an apparent give or take attitude toward drinking; and another 15% do not drink at all because they do not like the *effects*.

Interestingly, these same statistical figures have been found to hold true in our observations of monkeys. As we've already discussed, there is a facility in Oregon studying the alcohol consumption of monkeys when use is unrestricted. What is so interesting about observing the use of alcohol in monkeys is that it puts the psychosocial perspective of causation into question. How much weight should we really give to psychosocial variables when thinking about the possible causes of addiction? We must ask ourselves questions like: How are the heavy-using monkeys different from the limited-use and no-use monkeys and why? Are these monkeys suffering from emotional and social problems and why? Do these other factors really have anything to do with alcohol consumption or is it just a matter of the alcohol's effects on the brains of these monkeys being studied?

As it is, something like 50% of all addicts in treatment also have a mental health diagnosis. Whether these mental health disorders contributed to the development of addiction or whether they are the result of addiction we may never know. However it is clear that they only impact the consumption of use in relation to one's level of biological vulnerability (the effects they produce). It is apparent that psychological and emotional problems do not impact those with adverse or low levels of bio-vulnerability. This is confirmed by the fact that not all people with psychological and emotional problems ever succumb to chemical addictions.

The bottom line is this: troublesome life experiences and poor degrees of mental health can only cause *initiation* and use, but not necessarily addiction. This is because not everyone who tries a drug can become addicted. The possibility of addiction rests only in one's biological response to use. Therefore, psychosocial features can only play a role in the *development* of addiction. In other words, how much of a role psychological health and social influences play in the development of addiction depends primarily on individual attributes along with individually specific degrees of biological vulnerability. Genetic predisposition is the foundation of chemical addictions. Without a certain degree or level of biologic vulnerability addiction is not even possible. This is a fact we should never lose sight of while addressing all the other developmental problems and issues.

This is the main message of this book, and it is extremely important because it provides an understanding that is needed for a healthy and long-lasting recovery – A way of life that is more gratifying with each and every day of sobriety. This is why you are likely to hear many recovered addicts say that they are very grateful for having had their addiction, for without it they know they would have been doomed to a much lower quality of life, specifically in terms of contentment. In other words, if it were not for having to overcome their addiction, they know they would not have put the amount of work into personal growth and self-improvement as they did. This is what it took for them to achieve sobriety and the quality of life they enjoy today. It takes a great amount of humility and personal growth, not only to overcome an addiction, but to find the peace, joy, and happiness that makes it all worthwhile. They also realize that non-addicts do not have to pursue such degrees of personal growth, because without a reaction to a substance that calls for just a little more, they do not need to work on personal growth. It is through personal growth that addicts find the strength to abstain from using long enough to overcome their addiction for good.

Non-addicts can safely use a substance to relieve some of their anger and stress at times without placing themselves in danger of excessive use and physical dependence. It is often said that addicts cannot afford the luxury of anger and resentments like those who are non-addicts, and this appears to be quite true, especially in early recovery. And, as they learn to live without anger and resentments they find this to be a much better way to live. They know they would have been condemned to living a much lower quality of life if it were not for their addiction; this is why they become so grateful. This is another reason why acknowledging the differences between these two types of recovery, in-recovery vs. recovered, are so very important to understand.

There are those who, for whatever reasons, remain abstinent for years upon years only to relapse later in life. These addicts remain abstinent for many reasons without ever acknowledging their biological condition, and this lets them down time and time again. They cannot escape their desire-to-use because they never accepted it as their addiction. Their only focus was on not to use, and this is why their addiction, their abnormal desire-to-use, will continue to plague them from time to time. It was never addressed and killed with the knowledge of what *the drug* did to them and what it will always do to them, should they ever use again. This is why some do remain at risk of relapse indefinitely. This is a common result of the psychosocial perspective.

There are some *in-recovery* who have been referred to as dry drunks/addicts. They are usually pretty miserable because they hold onto all their negative worldly attitudes toward life; they are miserable because all they did was stop using. This is insufficient for any type of recovery because all the psychosocial adaptations that occur with addiction need to be addressed. These types learn to live without what they really want, their medication (their drug) which they see others using without recourse. This spurs jealously and they become filled with self-pity and an overwhelming sense that life is just not fair. This is because they have been forced into believing they are in some way less-than normal. They have been *forced to believe* that they have abused their God given right to use their drug by overdoing it. This stems from the teaching that brain damage is the source of addiction. Therefore, they must pay the price for all the perceived pleasure they are now missing out on. And they have to do this under the belief that they did this damage to themselves and are now mentally incapable of controlling their use. This is a lot to put on someone, and we wonder there is so much relapse!

By now you should be able to see how the psychosocial perspective contains numerous problems associated with its practical use. It's like shooting yourself in the foot – one step forward, two steps back. This may be a bold statement, but nearly every psychosocial intervention does not stand a chance of being useful and effective without a firm acknowledgment and solid acceptance of biological vulnerability. To recover without it, takes some great depths of surrender. Surrender, not only to the idea of self-causation, but to the idea of being less-than others, which is basically surrendering to the stigma of addiction. The degree of humility this calls for may be a wonderful opportunity for personal growth, but it is also a huge barrier. It is the main reason why so many addicts resist treatment for as long as they possibly can; and are, in essence, forced to reach some very low "bottoms" before they become willing to accept and work on their addiction.

As a result, those who do eventually surrender, are not necessarily surrendering to their addiction, for they still do not know what that is, they are only surrendering to the consequences of their use. I hope you see what is happening here. Under the psychosocial perspective they are being informed that their addiction is the "act of using," which not only reduces addiction to a mere behavioral problem, but is also the explanation given for their inability to cope effectively in life without using. In this way, they learn to stay sober without actually doing battle with their addiction. The lucky ones learn to suppress their desire to use, but never really overcome it. Adding insult to injury, they are informed that they did so much damage to their brains that they must now take care of their mental health indefinitely; that is, the only way they are to remain sober is to remain "in-recovery" forever! What a poor prognosis. What makes this perspective even more ineffective is that every addict *knows,* deep within their heart, that unless they were born into a different body, there was no way they could have avoided becoming an addict. This is likely to be the reason why the early alcoholics of AA stated,

"It did not satisfy us to be told that we could not control our drinking just because we were maladjusted to life, that we were in full flight from reality, or were outright mental defectives.... [even though] these things were true to some extent" (Alcoholics Anonymous, 2001, p. xxvi).

As you can plainly see, not much has changed in the past 80 years as far as causal perspectives are concerned. The psychosocial perspective is very counter-productive because it works against recovery in so many ways. Just the basis of it tears at a person's self-esteem, self-concept, and self-respect. It tells people it is not their fault on one hand, and then condemns them on the other. How would you feel if you were told your life experiences caused you to overindulge in drug use; that you were not to blame for turning to drug use under those circumstances; all the while knowing darn well not all people with similar experiences ever become addicts? Would you not feel less-than? Would you not believe you are in some way inferior, mentally impaired, or just sick in some unknown way forever? This is what the psychosocial perspective promotes with its *in-recovery* forever teachings. I have witnessed this belief in the stories of many addicts taught to believe they are always going to be in-recovery. This concept is so well accepted by treatment facilities across the nation that most all of them refer to any *re-covered* person as "those people in-recovery" - even state licensing agencies! This concept of recovery is actually a reflection of how poorly the psychosocial perspective addresses addiction in the first place.

The psychosocial perspective of always being at-risk for relapse, which also implies a degree of mental instability, is quite different from what the biological perspective promotes. The biological perspective is not only based on all the evidence that we have accumulated over the past few decades, but...

All it demands of those afflicted is to accept the fact that their biological reaction to their drug of use will never change.

In this most simple way, it prompts addicts to take responsibility for having their condition, not for causing it. This is how they begin to see that there is no way out. To give in to the desire-to-use would only produce more of the same results. It is out of their hands; and, if they want to improve their quality of life, and the lives of those close to them, the only way out is to stop using and to get over their desire-to-use. They need to shut the door on it.

While on the topic of genetic predisposition, this might be a good place to share another fascinating experiment. This one was performed with laboratory mice and presented by Michael Kuhar, the author of *The Addicted Brain* (2012). In his website broadcast through Emory University, he explains how dopamine levels are measured by inserting detection rods into the brains of mice. These rods can detect the concentration of dopamine in neurologic synapses. As many may already know, dopamine is one of the main neurotransmitters responsible for the pleasurable effects produced by psychotropic substances. All psychotropic substances greatly increase the amount of dopamine in synaptic clefts (the space between neurons where these cells are activated). Depending on the substance, dopamine levels can rise from 200 to 1100 percent. That's two to eleven times greater than the normal amount!

In this experiment, baseline measurements of dopamine levels were taken before the experiment. Then all the mice were continually injected with the same amount of a psychotropic substance until the researchers could be fairly certain that the brains of all these mice would be chemically altered. At this point the mice were titrated off the substance and the researchers kept track of how long it would take for the synaptic dopamine levels to return back to normal; back to their pre-experiment levels. Interestingly, some of these mice returned back to normal within three months. For others, it took six months and nine months. And for the remaining, their dopamine levels had not returned back to normal by the end of the experiment, which was 12 months later.

So, what did we learn from this experiment? Well, not only did it support what we already know, that genetics play an important role in addictions, but that some mice were more affected by the drug than the others. This suggested that more neurological change occurred in some of these mice than others, explaining why it took longer for some mice to return to normal dopamine baselines. In other words, it proved that their brains were indeed different in regards to the impact and effects of chemical substances. It also proved that their brains were pliable; that they do repair, but that it can take quite a bit more time for some than others. This experiment provided more evidence of varying degrees of resistance. Many other assumptive conclusions can be drawn, such as why some people become more addicted and why the development of addiction may be quicker for some than others, even when consuming the same amounts.

However, the real significance of this experiment lies in how it suggested that different degrees of biological adaptation occur in different mice. This is very likely to hold true for humans as well, as all animals are products of genes. This is just one of the hundreds or thousands of experiments that have been conducted over the past few decades, and this is very exciting stuff.

In addition, human brain imaging is reaching new levels of detection as well, and all this research is what is eventually going to change the way people view chemical addictions. There is so much to be learned here, and unless we can start to apply it, it might all go to waste. One DVD I can recommend for everyone to watch is called *Pleasure Unwoven* (2012) by Dr. Kevin McCauley (institute foraddictionstudy.com). Clips of it can be found on YouTube. The way he presents some of the science behind addictions makes it rather easy for most people to comprehend. We may not need to know exactly how all this scientific evidence is gathered, but we do need the ability to comprehend what it is telling us. This is so we can go out and apply it in the most ethical and effective manner possible.

As it is, our evidence is continuing to accumulate and grow at a steady pace, and unless our stubborn views of the past are questioned and addressed, the benefits of this knowledge may never become fully realized. It will remain on shelves collecting dust, just like those *ADDICTION* videos produced by NIDA and HBO in 2007 (hbo.com/addiction). Genetic predisposition is here to stay, so we better get on board with it. This is what the next chapter is all about. This is where we will take a look at how all three of the developmental factors of addiction, the bio-psycho-social aspects, come together in a more unified force.

MATRIX –
"Something within,
or from which something else
originates, develops,
or takes from"
– Merriam-Webster (2000)

Chapter 11

Bio-Psycho-Social Vulnerability

❧

When it comes to applying the biological, psycho-emotional, and socio-environmental causal aspects of addiction, it may be best to view them all together. In this way, we may be able to avoid the trap of attributing one's addiction to only one or two causal aspects and gain a more comprehensive understanding in the process.

Realizing that no one starts out with an addiction, we can look at where some people are in terms of vulnerability when they first begin using a psychotropic drug and compare this to where they may be in the present. This can give patients an idea of how much they have been affected by the drug, not only in terms of mental health, but in social and physical health as well. People who are addicted to drugs rarely improve in these areas, so we can be pretty sure there will be plenty of changes in these categories. These are the biopsychosocial adaptations.

Understandably, the more vulnerable some are to these adaptations with drug use, the more likely they would be to developing an addiction.

This is what the diagram on the next page is meant to explain by showing how all three biopsychosocial factors work together in the development of addictions; and possibly, the inevitability of addiction for some. From it you will be able to see how the biological factor plays the greatest role, and this is why it is the foundational cause of all chemical addictions. This takes us to the root of the problem, the place on which to build a solid and stable recovery.

These are the factors involved in using and it may be best to think of them in terms of how each one would impact use along a continuum. Everyone has different experiences in life and I have found that the use of this matrix can help people to understand how they could have possibly ended up with an addiction, even when they never thought it possible. This can be very insightful.

On this diagram the baseline continuums represent the impact or influence these factors have on using upon initiation. The adaptation continuums represent how much these factors have had on one's amount of consumption after a period of time, which would be the level of influence at the time of assessment (present).

THE BIO-PSYCHO-SOCIAL MATRIX

(–) ← Factors that Impact Use → (+)

No Use	Limited Use	Heavy Use	Addicted
15%	40%	30%	15%

Not Vulnerable - Low Vulnerability - At Risk (moderate) - High Vulnerability

Degree of Biological Vulnerability

←Negative Effects　　BASELINE – Effects upon initiation　　Positive Effects→

←High Resistance　　Adaptations – (Urges, Tolerance)　　Low Resistance→

Degree of Psycho-Emotional Vulnerability

←Well　　BASELINE – Wellness upon initiation　　Unwell→

←High Resistance　　Adaptations – Wellness in addiction　　Low Resistance→
(Internal)

Degree of Social-Environmental Vulnerability

←Low Influence　　BASELINE – Influence upon initiation　　High Influence→

←High Resistance　　Adaptations – Influence in addiction　　Low Resistance→
(External)

According to consumption rates, we know that about 45% of the population is at risk for alcoholism while another 55% is not, and this diagram may help to explain why only some of them will develop alcoholism. Keeping in mind that use causes addiction, it may be helpful to consider how all three of these biopsychosocial variables play into the development of chemical addictions. In doing so, we must also remember that *none of them are entirely independent of each other.* For example, one's desire-to-use may be ignited by an unavoidable circumstance, but whether or not they use will also depend on biological and psychological reactions.

Another important distinction exists in the depiction of 30 percent of heavy drinkers being at risk for alcoholism; this does not necessarily mean that each and every one of these high use drinkers are as biologically vulnerable to addiction as the others. Biological vulnerability is NOT a have- or have-not dichotomy, it's a degree of vulnerability along a continuum. Therefore, since this 30% are the ones who consume more alcohol, the greatest determinant of addiction would lie in how much of a resistance to neurological adaptation each one of these drinkers possess. Psycho-emotional and social-environmental factors can help to explain why this 30% drink more; however, most of them are not going to be as biologically vulnerable to addiction as some of the others. For those who do eventually develop alcoholism, small and unnoticeable neurological changes are probably taking place at a very slow rate with each and every use. This will not happen with the entire 30% of high use drinkers. In addition, there are also mental health issues and life-course circumstances that contribute to the development of addiction and not all 30% will be impacted in quite the same way by these variables either.

Now, for those closer to the middle point of the biological vulnerability continuum, those with a lower baseline of bio-vulnerability (limited use), the social and psychological factors would play a much greater role in the development of addiction for these people than they would for those with higher bio-vulnerability baselines. They may not be as biologically vulnerable to alcoholism as the high use group, but because it is the consumption of alcohol that actually causes addiction (the drug), these psychosocial factors would play a much greater role in their development of addiction.

Just like the fact that drugs produce different degrees of *effects* in everyone, biological *adaptation* can occur faster in some people than others, even with the same amount of consumption. As I have previously mentioned, different levels or degrees of biological adaptation explain why a 16 year old addict can experience alcoholic seizures upon withdrawal, while most others will never reach this degree of adaptation. As a point of interest, alcoholic grand-mal (tonic-clonic) seizures only occur in about 1% or less of all alcoholics. This is because most brains are more resistant to this type of neurological adaption. And, it is good to know that because of current detoxification precautions, only about 17% of this 1% type actually die from alcohol withdrawal.

BASELINES

The baselines (top lines) represent the point at which one is influenced by the factor involved at the start of use. This line represents the degree to which a person is affected by the use of a drug upon initiation. For instance, if a person loses all control of their consumption the very first time they drink alcohol, this initial *effect* from the alcohol might indicate an extremely high genetic vulnerability. Thus, they would be represented on the far right side of the continuum. Now, on the other hand, take a person whose reaction to first use is more moderate and who are not so intensely affected by the substance; they can pretty much take it or leave it and display some control over their consumption. They would be represented on the continuum closer to the middle. For those who are not impacted by the drug very much at all, they would be represented on the far left side of the continuum, the side of negative effects.

Likewise, on the other two baselines (top lines), the psycho-emotional and social-environmental continuums, these influences-to-use can be indicated along their prospective continuums as well. These baselines represent how much of an impact these variables would play in one's amount of consumption upon initiation of use. For example, a teen coming from an abusive or neglectful home may be more inclined to use more because of psycho-emotional problems. If a person started using in their teens and was raised by parents who used drugs and alcohol, they may be more inclined to use based on social-environmental influences; thus this could be indicated on the continuum farther to the right (low resistance). Take a person with no known psycho-emotional problems coming from a nuclear family that opposed drinking or drug use and they could would be represented on the left sides of the social and psychological continuums, with minimal influence-to-use (high resistance) factors.

In summation, the biological baseline represents how much _biological influence-to-use_ one is exposed to at the time of first use, such as the degree of initial _effects_ upon an individual (i.e., one's level of biological predisposition). This is displayed on the scale from negative to positive effects. The psychological baseline represents how much _psychological influence-to-use_ one is subject to at the time of first use, such as their state of mental and emotional well-being. This is displayed on a scale from well to unwell (i.e., one's level of psychological predisposition). The social baseline represents how much _social influence-to-use_ one is subject to at the time of first use (such as parents and friends who drink vs. those who don't) and other uncontrollable circumstantial situations, such as poverty, moving, or car accidents, etc. In this way, some people are more socially vulnerable to using than others (i.e., one's level of social predisposition). This is displayed on the scale from low to high influences for using.

ADAPTATIONS

Adaptations (bottom lines) represent the changes that are likely to occur over time, specifically to all three of the biopsychosocial variables that contribute to continued use. They represent the progression of the disease. The first thing to understand here is that _not all people are susceptible to all drugs._ This is why adaptations really only apply to those who have some degree of biological vulnerability to a specific substance. If a person dislikes a substance, psychological and social factors are very unlikely to influence a person's use, much less to the point of addiction. For those who have been using for a while, adaptations are bound to occur.

Biologically, one might develop high tolerance or withdrawal symptoms. Or, they may become physically dependent upon a substance where they may need to use to keep from getting sick. These adaptations can be reflected on the biological adaptation continuum, indicating how much change occurred between the baseline continuum and the adaptation continuum. People will use more due to biological adaptations.

On the Psycho-emotional adaptation continuum, changes in mental and emotional wellness can be applied in the same way. Those who are suffering more mental health problems than they were at the beginning of their use, can record this change along this line. As we know, mental health factors appear to be highly affected by drug use and account for about 50% of those in treatment. This is the one factor that may be the most affected by substance use, but that does not mean that poor psychological health can cause addiction without a good degree of biological vulnerability, it just keeps it going and must be treated. People will use more due to psycho-emotional adaptations.

For social-environmental adaptations, this would include various changes in one's social milieu, such as only having friends who use drugs and various accidents or traumas they may have experienced as a result of their use. On this continuum, how much resistance one may have against using would be indicated on this line. This social factor may start out as being a high resistance to use in the beginning, but over time may be reduced to a very low resistance, such as: only engaging in activities where using is permitted; engaging in dangerous activities; use-related jail time, etc., which all lower one's resistance to use. People will use more due to social-environmental adaptations.

These continuums may be quite different for each individual and it is best to have individuals decide for themselves where it is they fit on these lines. This can be a very insightful and useful tool, as it helps addicts understand the how and why of their condition. From them they will be able to see how much of a role each one of these factors may have played in the development of their own addiction. Ultimately, these considerations will not only help addicts to identify their addiction within, but may also help them come to the point of acceptance where they can then decide for themselves what they want to do about it – to put a halt to all these adaptations by addressing their addiction or to continue on. All in all, addiction is a biopsychosocial adaptation to drug use. This is why it is not only a physical condition of the brain, but a mental and social illness as well.

CONCEPTS

The first concept to understand here is that biological vulnerability does not apply to any substance but to the likelihood of any <u>specific substance</u> once tried or used. One person may be highly vulnerable to the effects of marijuana, but not to the effects of opiates and vice versa. This explains why some people who cannot stand the effects of marijuana and in no way could ever become addicted to that substance, could become highly addicted to another. The second concept to understand here is that not everyone is as vulnerable to either the effects or adaptations from the use of any specific substance, as others may be. For example, take a person high on the psychological and social baseline continuums, such as having a mental illness and coming from a family of substance users, and who never develops a chemical addiction. How do we explain this? Simple: this is because they have a lower degree of biological vulnerability to the substance in question. In other words, they do not have a reaction to a substance that supports use; or, they do not have enough of a biological vulnerability to ever become addicted, regardless of any psychological or social influences-to-use. As for psychosocial factors "causing" addiction, this is very unlikely. Despite similar personality characteristics among those with addictions, which have been thoroughly documented, there remains no evidence of an addictive personality actually causing addiction. In fact, there is no such thing as an "addictive personality." The similarities in personality traits we do see are most likely due to the psychosocial adaptations from use, rather than being an actual cause for use. However, these psychosocial personality traits, such as a powerful attitude toward using, could be indicated on the psychosocial baselines and still play a major role in the continuation and further development of addiction.

Lastly, when we consider the fact that drugs cause addiction in those who are biologically vulnerable, it explains how and why addiction rates increase with an increase in social acceptance. For example, if a person is only somewhat biologically vulnerable to alcohol and lives in a social environment that encourages excessive drinking, they are likely to ingest more alcohol than they would if they were not in that environment. Being somewhat vulnerable to the effects of alcohol they are more likely to develop alcoholism on the basis of psychosocial variables. With some degree of biological vulnerability, any one of these psychosocial variables within this matrix can lead to more and more use and can set the progression of alcoholism into motion, possibly increasing the alcoholism rates of a population as a whole. However, alcoholism rates can only increase to the extent of how many people within a population are biologically vulnerable to the effects of alcohol. Some may be highly vulnerable, and others may be moderately vulnerable, but it all comes down to the effects of a drug on the whole person, biologically, psychologically, and social-environmentally.

All that is really needed for a chemical addiction to develop appears to be an idiosyncratic response to use (i.e., intensity of effects and the inability of the brain to return to normal neurological functioning after use). This is made evident through all the scientific research and animal studies we have available to us today; however, this does not mean that psycho-emotional health does not play a significant role in the development of chemical addictions. Psychosocial responses to use incite more use; more use incites more biological adaptation; more biological adaptation incites more psychosocial adaptation; and on and on it grows in a progressive downward spiral with each using factor (influence-to-use) fueling the other using factors.

CORRELATION –
"A relation existing between
phenomena or things... which
tend to vary, be associated, or
occur together in a way not
expected on the basis of
chance alone"
– Merriam-Webster (2000)

Chapter 12

Spiral Progression

We often think of progression in a linear sense, such as the way Jellinek presented it with a dip in the line to represent greater degrees of chemical dependence. However, since the progression of addiction involves multiple factors that feed off each other, it may be more helpful to think of it as a reciprocal interaction.

CIRCULAR PROGRESSION
Consumption + Adaptations = Severity of Addiction

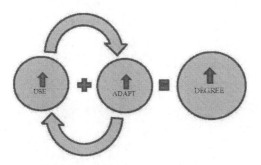

This diagram is meant to show how biological and psycho-social adaptations (adapt circle) fuel more and more use (use circle); which of course leads to greater and greater degrees of addiction over time (degree circle). It can help us to understand the bi-directional relationship between use and adaptation. As one's use increases, so does all three biopsychosocial adaptations, and as one's adaptations increase, so does one's using. Because of this, a negative correlation exists between use and all three bio-psycho-social factors. For example, as one's use increases ↑ there is a decline ↓ in mental health, and as mental health declines ↓ there is an increase ↑ in use. This is what occurs in those who develop chemical addictions.

Addiction starts with the initiation of first use and the experience of intense degrees of effect. These effects will determine the likelihood of repeated use, primarily on the basis of positive reinforcement. Quantity and frequency of use will be influenced by how much of an impact the drug has on a person. People who experience high tolerance and/or loss-of-control with first use are probably more genetically predisposed to addiction than those who are not as highly affected. As shown in the baseline continuum diagram, all three biopsychosocial factors will play a role in quantity and frequency of use. And, since use causes addiction (in those vulnerable), this diagram is another way to understand each factor's role or impact on the development of addiction. This does not mean anyone can become addicted to a chemical substance. The possibility of addiction is solely dependent upon the *effects* a drug can produce within the individual. These effects impact quantity and frequency of use, and they include psychological, social-environmental and biological vulnerabilities. In other words, with more psychological and social adaptation there will be more and more use, resulting in more and more biological adaptation (primarily damage); and, with more biological adaptation there will be more and more psychosocial adaptation. Thus, with more biopsychosocial adaptation, the greater degree of addiction one will experience.

This is a cycle of interaction where each factor feeds off the other factors and fuels the progression; and, because of biological predisposition to neurological adaptations, which have been clearly confirmed, it is an awfully hard cycle to break. The good news is; it is possible. This explains why recovery must start with abstinence. Unless a person is sober, they cannot work on all the psychosocial adaptations that accompany addiction. And, if left unaddressed, these adaptations will lead the person right back into using. When it comes to understanding the development and severity of addictions it may be helpful to visualize the progression as a three dimensional cone-shaped spiral. Thus the old adage of "spiraling out of control" appears to be rather fitting.

SPIRAL PROGRESSION
Initiation of use

Occasional Use
(Abnormal effects)

No Addiction
(Vulnerability)

Increased Frequency
(Abnormal response)

Moderate Addiction
(BPS adaptations)

Heavy Use

Severe Addiction

In progression, it is important to realize that although one may not be addicted right from the start, the addiction is likely to start with the initiation of first use. Here we can visualize how neurological changes are likely to be occurring at levels far below conscious awareness long before the addiction becomes readily apparent. Thus, addicts become addicted to various substances because, (1) neurological changes occur with each use, and (2) they are not likely to return to pre-neurological functioning after use (which is supported by animal experiments). One's ability to return to pre-use neurological functioning clearly depends upon one's individual level of resistance to biological change (biological vulnerability). Therefore, the reason only some people become addicted to drugs is because of individual degrees of biological predisposition in relation to their amount of use. The problem is, nobody knows what is going on inside their brain or how much biological adaptation may be occurring before it is too late. This is why we cannot hold addicts responsible for causing their own additions. Individual use is dependent upon many factors, but underlying it all is a biological reaction that no one has any control over.

I realize this may sound rather shocking to some people, as it goes against what so many people have believed for so long – the axiom that all people have a choice of whether or not to use, which is only a partial truth; however, for the addict, it is more likely that they only did what came most natural to them – they had no reason not to use. Well, not until it became a problem, but by then it would have been too late, for the addiction would have set in. This is what we all need to understand if we are going to be of help to those suffering. Yes, early life traumas, degrees of mental health, emotional health, sexual abuse, physical abuse, etc., all play a part in the development of addiction, but only because of the person's individual level of biological predisposition. For those without a relatively high biological predisposition to a particular substance the probability of other problems causing their addiction is highly unlikely.

Nobody can control whether or not they would become an addict, and addicts need to hear and know this; otherwise, they will blame their addiction on past misfortunes, people they know, or anything they can, including themselves. This is only natural; however, this way of thinking will only hinder the clients' recovery. It only serves to feed self-pity and anger, even if they believe they caused their own addiction they can become angry at themselves. This, or any anger, leads to relapse because any amount of stress put upon the limbic system will ignite strong urges and obsessive thoughts to use. It is not even good for addicts to get angry at their drug because this will only last for a little while. Remember, addicts love their drug and they always will. They must learn to accept this and take responsibility for the condition they have, not for causing it. And, they cannot take responsibility for it until they know their addiction is a real physical and psychological condition. Early AAs instinctively knew this, but it has taken until now for science to actually prove it. It was this acceptance of having a biological reaction, which the founders of Alcoholics Anonymous referred to as an allergy, that made AA such a huge success.

Sad to say, but the foundational acknowledgement of this biological reaction has fallen by the wayside in the rooms of AA today. Over the years, with the influx of new members coming from treatment facilities, and bringing with them the psycho-social causational beliefs they undoubtedly, and probably unconsciously, picked up there, this most important aspect of recovery appears to have been swept under the carpet. However, and thanks to our new scientific discoveries, I suspect it will be making its way back. After all, this was the "knowledge" that Bill Wilson talked about. And, it was this biological knowledge that AA was founded on.

Other biological evidence has been discovered over the years, and no book on the causal aspects of addiction would be complete without the mention of Tetrahydroisoquinoline (THIQ). This is an interesting story because back in the 1970's THIQ was only known to be found in the brains of heroin addicts. However, this all changed when a student accidently found THIQ in the brains of dead alcoholics. According to David L. Ohlms (1983), this student was Virginia Davis and he gives a colorful account of how she found this. She was examining the still warm corpses of recently deceased homeless alcoholics being picked up off city streets. The interesting thing about this discovery is that THIQ was not expected to be found in alcoholics, for how could it get there if it was a by-product of an opiate? Well, apparently THIQ is something the brain can make on its own, which we now know to be the case. Confusingly, it was not found in the brains of deceased drinkers, but only known alcoholics, and more recently in some "non-drinkers," which adds to even more confusion. This led many to discard the use of this information altogether, but regardless, this is more evidence that something at the biological level is occurring quite differently between non-alcoholic drinkers and alcoholics. According to David L. Ohlms, in his book, *The Disease Concept of Alcoholism* (1983), he reported that when a small amount of THIQ was injected into the brains of rats, they become alcoholic (Fonda, 2009). However, this finding was hard to replicate in further experiments. So, it appears that THIQ is not the sole and single determinant of alcoholism. This is not surprising. Nor is the fact that THIQ was found in the brains of some "non-drinkers." Neither of these findings nullify the significance of this biological evidence in any way. It does however, raise many more questions as to the role of THIQ in the development of addictions. Recovered heroin addicts and non-drinkers who have recovered from alcoholism have THIQ in their brains, and if a potential alcoholic with THIQ in their brain does not drink, that does not mean that THIQ doesn't play a significant role in the development of alcoholism. As it is, the correlation between THIQ and addiction still remains to be rather significant, and may just be another indication of higher genetic or biological susceptibility. More research needs to be done here.

What captures my attention is; how can such hardcore evidence like this be totally ignored when it comes to treatment? As it is, most patients currently in treatment will never hear of THIQ, which is evidence to the fact that the brains of addicts are quite different from the brains of non-addicts. And, if we continue to ignore evidence that does not suit our own beliefs, or our liking, we will be forever in ignorance. Therefore, we must thoroughly examine all the evidence we have, even if we don't like it.

PHENOMENON -
"An observable fact or event...
of scientific interest susceptible
to scientific description
and explanation"
- Merriam-Webster (2000)

Chapter 13

Focus of Treatment

It is well documented that the children of alcoholics are three to five times more likely to develop alcoholism than children of non-alcoholics. This may sound like a lot, but it actually equates to only about one in every four to five children of alcoholic parents becoming alcoholic themselves (Overview of, n.d.). This is pretty good evidence that genetics play a significant role in the cause of addiction. However, many would attribute the cause of this phenomenon to be the passing down of psychosocial attributes; such as, using attitudes, lifestyle choices, and character traits. However, there is a huge problem with this reasoning. Addiction is not something anyone seeks. It is something everyone tries to avoid, especially children of alcoholics. For those raised in alcoholic homes, the last thing they would ever allow themselves to be (if they could avoid it) is alcoholic, and yet it happens much more often in these families than it does for those not raised in alcoholic homes. This is why we must turn to our evidence and approach treatment from a biological standpoint, making clear distinctions between what is, and what is not, addiction.

The evidence we have today provides us with a very sound explanation for all the phenomena we have observed in addiction over the years. However, in order to apply it effectively, it may help to understand these few basic truths about chemical addictions. I call them the **BEAR Basics:**

Addictions are...

Biologically Conceived

- Genetics determine degrees of neurological reaction – *effects*
- Psychosocial factors are *dependent* upon biological effects

Emotionally Centered

- Chemical addictions reside in one's "heart" – *core of the brain*
- Evidenced by *changes* in the Mesolimbic System (e.g., NAcc,)

Adaptation Driven

- Genetics determine degrees of resistance to *bio-adaptations*
- Psychosocial adaptations are *responses* to biological effects

Recoverable

- Complete Recovery – Adaptations are *not permanent*
- Neurological *reactions* to specific drugs are permanent

We have all heard the saying, "Addicts can never use safely ever again," but we never really knew why until now. We have just accepted this observation as proof of what the addict has done to themselves through self-induced brain damage. Since we now know that addiction is caused by the drug, we can understand that this is what the drug will always do (to the vulnerable person). A person's level or degree of vulnerability does not improve with abstinence. If anything, it gets worse. The majority of addicts who try to use safely after a period of abstinence fall right back into their addiction and end up more addicted than they were prior to a period of abstinence. They end up more addicted because they not only reactivate their addiction biologically, but they sink farther and farther into their addiction psychosocially. It appears that once the brain has adapted to a drug neurologically (as what occurs in addiction), and the brain has had a period of time to heal (such as in dopamine levels returning to normal), the brain can adapt to the same type of substance much more easily when it is reintroduced in the future. Psychologically, the addict is ecstatic to once again feel the relief they found in their substance; however, like a double edged sword, they are bound to feel even worse about themselves and their inability to control their use; thus, contributing to even more psychosocial adaptation. Consequently, they end up with even more desire-to-use and less hope and faith in being able to recover than they had prior to abstinence; thus, more addicted.

The following chart illustrates the difference between addressing addictions from the psychosocial perspective, where the focus of treatment is on changing one's behavior (left), and the biological perspective, where the focus of treatment is placed on repairing all the biopsychosocial (BPS) damage (right). When the biological cause of addiction is taught and thoroughly accepted it is much easier to focus on repair instead of all the guilt and shame embedded in the psychosocial perspective. Under the psychosocial perspective, to use is to cause and to stop using is to stop causing; thus, guilt and shame cannot be avoided. The following chart may help to clarify these differences.

BEHAVIOR VS. CONDITION

Addiction as Behavior	ADDICTION BIO-PERSPECTIVE	Addiction as Condition
PSYCHOSOCIAL FOCUS STOP CAUSES		BIOLOGICAL FOCUS BPS REPAIR
SOCIAL Life Course causes--------> (Developmental)	Fuels Use in Bio-vulnerable People	
	↓	BIO-PSYCHO-SOCIAL REHABILITATION
MEDICAL (BIO) **Drugs cause addiction**-----> (Abstinence/Medication)	-------------------->	--------------------------------
	∧	Repair the BPS Damage Abstinence MH Problems Emotional Distress
MH (PSYCHO) Deficiency causes--------> (Cognition)	Fuels Use in Bio-vulnerable People	Self-pity Social Isolation Coping Skills Stress Tolerance Anger Expression Emotional Maturity Depression Eliminate Excuses
PREMISE Stop Behavior = Stop Addiction		**PREMISE** Repair Damage = Stop Addiction

For example, I recently observed a psychotherapy group where the clients' self-identified values (e.g., family, finance, sobriety, etc.) were used as a ploy to scare, guilt, and shame clients into staying sober (stop causing); this is when they were instructed to throw their hand written values into a garbage can! This was done as a representation of what they would be doing to them-selves if they were to use again (instead of being encouraged to hold on to them dearly and further their personal growth through identification and rediscovery – rehabilitation). This is just one example of how causational beliefs affect how therapy is applied; however, it affects nearly every intervention. In other words, the focus and purpose of any given intervention is likely to be guided by causational beliefs. In this case, it is plain to see the insinuations embedded and the implications of these tactics. In others, they are not so obvious, but they are still there.

What is the use of gaining a more accurate and beneficial perception of addiction if we are left with nothing but our old ineffective approaches? Placing the focus of treatment on repairing all the biopsychosocial damage caused by the addiction, rather than on stopping the behavior of using does wonders for those addicted. First and foremost, it helps to relieve all the shame and guilt those in treatment are likely to be experiencing. This does not mean all the psychosocial problems do not have to be addressed, for obviously, this is where most of the rehabilitative work needs to be done.

However, even if all the biopsychosocial factors were to be addressed in treatment, it would still not be very effective if the addiction is not being addressed directly. This is the most important part of effective treatment and it is the part that is most often ignored. Not intentionally, but more through the *assumption* that clients would make these connections on their own; the connection between reasons for using and their own individual and intrinsic need, their desire-to-use. This is why it is imperative to assist clients in identifying their addiction within and help them to distinguish the difference between their rational reasons for not using, which resides in their mind (frontal cortex thought), and their desire-to-use which resides in their "heart" (the core, or limbic structures of the brain). This is where every addict must do battle with their addiction. To just *assume* that every addict in treatment is making this connection on their own can be a very big mistake. Chances are, their ability to think clearly and makes these kinds of rational connections are beyond them in early recovery. As previously discussed, it can take months, or even years, for the brain to gain back its clarity of thought, if it does at all; for the brain becomes very clouded in addiction.

To elaborate, the desire-to-use resides in the heart and soul of the addict and not only in the urges and cravings experienced in early recovery. What many providers fail to recognize and address is that this biological desire-to-use remains within the addict indefinitely. That is, until it is acknowledged, addressed, and purposely fought. Brain imaging studies have verified that even after three months of abstinence, visual cues of drugs and using paraphernalia activate neurological structures in the limbic system of the brain (believed to be the source of biological cravings) that do not activate in non-addicts (Psychiatry, 2015). Unless this most basic instinctual drive is identified and acknowledged by the client, all the psychosocial treatment in the world will not help. For the addict, their drug was the only thing on God's green earth that they could count on with absolute certainty; unlike people, money, and circumstances, it never let them down. This is what needs to be remembered, as well as taught. It is like a bad love affair, a nemesis. When use is denied, the desire-to-use is sure to follow. *This is what the addict must battle: their mind against their heart.* Their heart is absolutely crushed at the thought of not having their drug. This is why we cannot just *assume* any addict wants to quit using on their own, even if they say they do. Nearly all addicts go through a phase of only wanting the consequences to stop, not their use. Deep inside they desperately want to find any way possible they can continue using without having any consequences. This is why the addiction must be addressed separately. We cannot expect any addict to fight a battle if they do not know what the enemy is – if they do not know what addiction is. When asked, their reply is often, "using despite consequences," which is not even close. This is just a symptom of addiction; addiction lies much deeper. It is a desire that is imbedded into the core of the addict's existence.

This is why identifying the addiction within is going to take a lot of work. As previously mentioned, some addicts can stop using for long periods of time (when they have to) even while having a *desire-to-use*. This is why they must learn to identify the feelings that accompany this desire, which are innumerable. For example, when they get strong cravings and urges to use, they must learn to ask themselves, "What is it that I am feeling? Am I hungry, angry, lonely, tired, scared, stressed out, depressed, excited, etc., etc., etc." They must learn that their reaction to these ever so normal feelings, which is to use, is actually quite *abnormal*. They must learn that their reaction to the drug itself, with the intense effects and loss-of-control it produces in them is quite *abnormal*. And, they must learn about all the various ways in which their addiction to a substance has negatively impacted their biopsychosocial health, including their inability to experience pleasure without using and changes in tolerance and withdrawal. Behind the desire-to-use lies a physical need and a mental obsession to fulfill this need.

Many who have not reached severe levels of psychological and physical dependence along the progression, can stop using for months at a time and this is very confusing to them; to be told they have an addiction when they know they can stop. These are the people who come in and out of treatment until the progression gets the best of them (i.e., until they hit bottom). Again, this is why the addiction must be addressed separately from all the psychosocial problems and issues that propagate use.

The goal of treatment should not be to merely stop using, which is too often the main focus of treatment in the psychosocial perspective – implied, insinuated, or otherwise. Putting a halt to using behavior does not stop the addiction. This is only remission, not recovery. Addressing the addiction is what helps addicts to see they have a serious and progressive illness. This is why addiction can also be called a disease (although I prefer the term condition).

The condition of biological vulnerability is permanent and progressive if left untreated. When addicts recognize, acknowledge, and accept their condition, and the permanency of it, it serves as a natural motivator. They no longer just want to put an end to the consequences of their use; they want to escape the persistent call to use. Eventually, they finally realize they have to break off their love affair with the drug. And, breaking off a love affair with a drug is very hard and can take years to completely get over. In the process, most will pass through at least some of Kubler-Ross's five stages of grief (i.e., denial, anger, bargaining, depression, and acceptance), and Bridges' (2004) three phases of transition (endings, neutral zone, and new beginnings). This can be a very solemn and depressing time for some. For those who succeed and are freed from their desire-to-use, they are indeed recovered. They've earned it, and are therefore no longer in recovery. This does not mean they forget how much they loved the effects of their drug. Nor do they forget their condition; their response to the drug. They know what the drug does to them, and because they have accepted their condition and no longer doubt they have a very real and abnormal reaction to their drug (the condition), they know what their drug will do to them if they were ever start using again. This is what really keeps these people sober, nothing else.

Maintaining a recovery program, such as attending AA or staying away from drinking establishments is good, and probably needed in the beginning, but this is not what keeps people sober for any real length of time. Of those who recover, they are like the person who loves strawberries, but because they are allergic to them they have no interest in them anymore. This is why fully recovered addicts can learn to be around drugs and alcohol without getting the desire-to-use. If the thought of using crosses their mind from time to time, as can be expected, they dismiss it as plain foolishness, just like the person who is allergic to strawberries. Believe it or not, even people with food allergies have thoughts of eating their poison from time to time and they have to remind themselves of why they cannot indulge. It is the same for recovered addicts.

In the following chart I have outlined the difference between treating the addiction and treating all the psychological problems associated with addiction. This is important. When we realize and accept that mental health issues cannot cause addiction in and of themselves, we can also see how useless and detrimental it can be to make any reference to them as being the cause of one's addiction.

I hope looking at treatment in this way might help to make it clear that treating addiction and treating all the psychological issues associated with addiction are two very different things. In other words, addressing all the psychosocial issues associated with addiction is not a direct treatment of addiction, nor should it be stated, implied, or insinuated that these mental health issues *are* addiction, and especially not the cause of addiction. I cannot emphasize this enough. Included in this suggestion is not to imply, or insinuate, that any of a person's personal problems or life-course experiences caused them to become an addict (e.g., abusive parents, rape, sexual abuse, poverty, etc.), even though these issues are very likely to spur on more use. Some biologically vulnerable people may not have become addicted if it were not for these contributing factors; however, it should be made perfectly clear that these things, in and of themselves, cannot cause addiction; they only play a part in the development of addiction because of biological vulnerability.

ADDICTION & MENTAL HEALTH

Addressing Addiction	Addressing Mental Health
PREPARING FOR BATTLE	STRENGTH FOR BATTLE
Teach what addiction is: Bio-cravings/mental obsession Loss-of-control & dependence Tolerance & withdrawal Resides in midbrain (heart/soul)	Address lack of development issues: Assist clients in identifying feelings – emotional growth Assist clients in establishing own values – finding purpose Assist clients in expressing anger in a positive way Assist clients in coping with and overcoming depression Assist clients in coping w/fears
Teach what causes addiction: Drugs!!! (for those vulnerable to:) B-P-S baseline effects B-P-S adaptations from use	
Assist in identifying addiction: Living for use after work Living for use on the weekends Finding excuses to use Inability to be present Just a little more phenomenon Abnormal hangovers/ none Soul-wrenching cry for more Lack of non-using activities Inability to control or cut-down External controls on use Persistent psycho problems Physical problems (liver, etc.) Lack of interests & goals	Address effects of addiction: Emotional instability Cognitive dissonance Irrational & invading thoughts Control issues/only if's Self-centeredness Tendency to manipulate Lack of honesty with self & others Lack of forgiveness Self-justifications/blaming Self-pity – victimization Negative attitudes/outlook Sway of grandiosity & inferiority Low self-esteem, etc.
Addiction	**Not Addiction**

It is clear that people with addictions must be biologically vulnerable to a drug's effects and adaptations first; otherwise all people who experience these tough and horrendous times would all be addicts, which is obviously not the case. Patients must be taught this *truth* because it helps to remove any excuse for continued use based on the blaming of others in their life and the unfortunate situations they may have been exposed to. These are disruptive traps they desperately need to avoid. Placing blame on anything other than biological vulnerability just doesn't work; it only creates victims, and this is never a good thing.

All too often, many well-intentioned treatment providers are actually supporting and perpetuating victimization and poor mental health *as addiction* by the way they provide treatment. This is what happens when the counselor believes addiction is a behavioral problem that arises out of a need for drugs in order to cope with life; and, probably because they could see themselves doing this exact same thing if they had the troublesome lives of some of their patients. In the words of H. M. Tomlinson, "We see things not as they are, but as we are." This is the real problem. Since all addicts have experienced some very troubling times, either before or after their addiction set in, this is very easy to do. However, it is not like this at all. Most addicts experience much more emotional pain and suffering during or after the development of their addiction than ever before it.

Even though it is clear that we need to support and reinforce the need for taking responsibility for the condition, unless we start to view addiction as being a separate entity, independent of mental health issues, these causational insinuations are likely to remain. Those with addictions are not unintelligent and there is nothing wrong with their brains. So, even if left unstated, addicts will pick up on and readily accept these same types of logical conclusions. When it comes to mental health, there is usually nothing wrong with the brains of those with addictions. They actually work very well. In other words, when it comes to the actual functionality of the brain, they are usually not damaged at all. They are likely to be a little clouded, but not necessarily damaged. This is remarkable, but this is actually what makes recovery possible.

What is more likely to be responsible for all the mental health issues associated with addictions are all the psychological adaptations that are bound to come with the continual use of a perception changing (psychotropic) substance – specific ways of thinking that are detrimental to mental health and wellness. These are neurological pathways that have become automatic responses and they can be halted; they can be unlearned and replaced with new ways of thinking. When new and healthier ways of thinking are learned and practiced they too will become automatic responses. This will take a lot of time and effort. What we are talking about here is the creation of new neurological pathways, new ways of thinking. Addressing these mental health issues are of utmost importance because this is where addicts will find the strength, courage, and hope to fight off their addictions.

Personal problems and tough life-course experiences can cause depression, self-pity, victimization, fears, anxiety, PTSD, and a whole list of psychological problems; however, they do not cause addiction. They may incite more use, and may even send some over the edge from a previously held perception of self-control, but they cannot cause addiction in and of themselves. These problems only spur on more use in addicts because of the comfort they can only receive from their drug. This is because the emotional center of the brain has been biologically altered. They cannot withstand the normal challenges of life without using because of this. And, they must know this. They must know how the drug has impacted them differently. Knowing this *truth* will help them to face their addiction head on by removing any excuses to use. They do not need anybody providing them with any excuses, no matter how logical they may appear, or in a misguided attempt to divert blame and show empathy – doing so can cause some irreparable damage. This can lead many an addict astray; to great depths of despair, even suicide. If they are lucky enough to return to treatment, it will most likely be a result of reaching some very low "bottom," which makes it even that much harder for them to recover. Even worse, is trying to teach them different ways to view their addiction once they have been taught and internalized psycho-social explanations, which is what happens to those who have been in and out of treatment numerous times.

ADDRESSING ADDICTION

Now, let's return to the *Addressing Addiction* side of the chart. After clients have identified the addiction they have, there are many more steps they will need assistance with. They will need to overcome the stigma of addiction so they can be okay with having the condition of addiction. They will have to learn to accept the addiction as their own, and this is something that cannot be ignored. It will not go away on its own. They will have to accept the permanence of their condition and be willing to take on the responsibility of having to do something about it. They may also need to overcome some ambivalence regarding whether or not they want to do anything about it at all. They must learn, and accept, that they have a progressive illness; that there is no other way out. They must learn how their addiction affects the people they love, and that it is not just their problem. After they finally accept their condition they must make a decision to do something about it. This is not a onetime deal for the addict. They may need to make this same decision one hundred times a day and be prepared to stay on course for months or even years at a time. To do this, they will have to have the strength to tell themselves no, over and over again. This is a battle only they can fight. If they have any doubt whether or not their condition is real or permanent, or that it is only in their head, they will slip and use. If they have not gained a strong enough *belief* in these matters, as well as enough faith in the possibility of recovery, they will most likely slip and fall right back into full relapse. And, the more a person relapses, the harder it is for them. Relapse, although common, does not have to be a part of recovery (Remember the well-educated man example?).

Clearly there is a lot of work in treating addictions, and this left side of the chart only presents the focus of treatment up to the decision making stage. Then the patient will have to make a commitment, learn recovery tools and practice recovery skills, all of which will require some assistance and can be learned through therapeutic techniques and exercises. Merely providing mental health treatment alone is insufficient for treating addiction. And, it can be much worse be if they are led into believing poor psycho-emotional health is the foundational cause of their addiction.

Recovery is a process and assisting clients in identifying their addiction is only the first step. It is important to realize that when clients enter treatment they are not even close to being in recovery. They are merely in treatment, and that is whether they are still using or not. Abstinence and recovery are two very different things. Most addicts are very familiar with the suffering that goes along with having an addiction and those periods of abstinence that cannot be avoided; this often leads them into thinking they are not addicts; and therefore, they do not need treatment. As long as they can hold on to some hope of ever using again they will likely tell you anything they think you want to hear. Whether they know it or not, most addicts are masters at manipulation. Chances are, they have been manipulating people for many years and treatment professionals are only in their way. For many, they honestly believe they are not hurting anyone but themselves, which is their God given right, and therefore they should be left alone.

As you may have noticed, I used the word *battle* to signify what is required of each addict in order to gain recovery. Nobody can fight this battle for them, and as far as I know, recovery has never been gained without it. This is why it is so important to address all the psychosocial issues associated with addiction. This is where they will gain the strength to fight the battle deep within, the fierce battle between what is in their *mind* and *heart*, the soul-wrenching plea for their drug. It is like divorcing a spouse for abuse, although I suspect it may even be a little harder. This is because one's drug, although very abusive at times, has never let them down. As I mentioned earlier, it was the only thing on God's green earth they could depend on completely; as it was always there to make them feel better, which it always did until the drug's abuse, by whatever means, led them into treatment.

Much more can be said about the benefits of applying the biological perspective to the remaining stages of recovery. Knowing the stages of recovery is very important because they help to guide the focus of treatment toward what is needed at each stage along the way. This is another reason why biological vulnerability is so very important; it is a very plausible explanation, supported by scientific evidence, which patients are much more willing to accept, and the acceptance stage is an essential stage of recovery. It is not about what you or I can accept as a reasonable explanation. It is not even about what can or cannot be proven. That is irrelevant. The important consideration here is to know which one will be most beneficial to the patient. Therefore, ask yourself; which perspective has more evidence to support it? Which perspective is more effective? Isn't this what treatment is all about? How to best serve and treat those with chemical addictions?

ADDRESSING MENTAL HEALTH

This is a very important part of treatment, for without it clients will not gain the minimal psycho-emotional strength and courage to battle their condition, nor would they be very likely to gain any degree of satisfaction in life without it. These issues are usually addressed in group therapy. This is where unconscious and dysfunctional personality traits can be addressed. In some cases individual psychotherapy may be more appropriate for treating more intimate and personal issues. Group therapy is the main course of action and plenty of books have been written on its use and effectiveness in treating addictions. Irvin Yalom's and Gerald Corey's approaches to group psychotherapy are two excellent cases in point.

For this reason, I will not go into much detail about treating mental health issues here, other than to reinforce the notion that causational responsibility may only apply to psychological distress, not to addiction. Also, since most of addiction treatment is conducted in group therapy, I think it is important to briefly touch upon the group leader's responsibilities in regards to directing and reinforcing the concepts I have been presenting. Chances are, most addicts, if not all, will come into treatment with their own preconceived notions about addiction and these may need to be addressed and corrected as they arise. The one leader function that is of utmost importance and which is often ignored, is an explicit explanation as to why clients are placed in group therapy; what it is they are attempting to achieve there and how they are going to obtain what they need. All too often it is as if they are given no explanation at all and are just expected to trust in the process, about which they know nothing (e.g., this is how we do it).

For those who may be a little unsure of what group therapy is all about, or would like a little review of what is intended, I suggest referring to the *Mechanism of Action* in Yalom's book entitled *The Theory and Practice of Group Psychotherapy (5th ed.)*, page 62. Here you will find a list of Carl Roger's deep insights into the benefits of a truly therapeutic relationship, and group therapy is no different. This is how group therapy works and achieves the benefits of improved psycho-emotional health. As you read through this list of therapeutic processes, you will see how one can make use of, and apply: Yalom's therapeutic factors, Freud's defense mechanisms, cognitive distortions, cognitive dissonance, reality testing, and gaining awareness of feelings, unconditional positive self-regard, humility, and authenticity. Group therapy is a very useful tool for personal growth, which can be achieved through honest and sincere self-examination through interactions with others.

Improvement of psycho-emotional health is one purpose of group therapy. But in addition to all that can be achieved through addressing multiple mental health issues is what we can learn about ourselves through self-disclosure and appropriate feedback. Although much can be achieved (and despite alternate beliefs), group psychotherapy is not about solving problems for people. It is about having them get in touch with themselves, gaining self-awareness, and learning better coping methods as a result. It is through group therapy one can learn to identify the addiction deep within and work through all the stages of recovery. All counselors have their own style, and many excellent counselors are very skilled in this area. However, it is important that they explain the how and why of group therapy to their clients. Providing confusing and vague explanations to the how and why of group therapy can be just as detrimental as providing clients with vague and confusing explanations as to the how and why of addiction.

People with addictions usually have a distorted perception of themselves. So, while we are on the subject of what group therapy is all about, I would like to share with you a diagram from Taylor (2008) that gives us a visual illustration of just how one's self-concept is likely to improve through self-awareness, honesty, and humility; all of which develop and grow through interactions with others.

SELF-CONCEPT

(Self-esteem – Identity – Self Image – Role Performance)

HIGH – Self-esteem

| Actual | | X-----------X | | Ideal |
| Self | X---X | | | Self |

LOW – Self-esteem

(Dochterman & Bulerchek, 2004; cited in Taylor, 2008)

This is a diagram of self-perception. The closer one's self-concept is to reality, the higher one's self-esteem is going to be. And, the more distant one's self-concept is from reality, the lower their self-esteem is going to be. This is a prime example of how group therapy works. As patients become more comfortable and at ease with other members of their group, they are going to disclose more about themselves. This leads to more chances for them to gain insight about themselves and correct the distortions and delusions they may be harboring. This process can be guided and enhanced through client feedback and facilitated interventions (on the next couple of pages). This is where the therapist can take an active role in bringing attention to the various thoughts, feelings, and behaviors that are likely to be hindering a patient's growth in recovery, from which all members can benefit. It is also an excellent opportunity for the therapist to model appropriate behaviors in setting group norms, partake in self-disclosure by sharing their own thoughts and feelings about what is occurring in the here and now, as well as (according to the biological perspective), disclosing any past history of addiction, as this will only add to the cohesiveness of the group and benefit clients in all the ways discussed in Chapter 9.

In chemical addictions, and primarily because of the use of psychotropic (perception-changing) substances, it is common, if not the rule, that most addicts become very self-delusional and self-protected. And, just to make a point here, this is why chemical addictions are unlike any other so-called addiction that does not involve perception changing drugs. Years of exposure to these kinds of drugs can cause one's perception of self and others, as well as to the world in which they live, to become severely distorted. So, starting below, and on the next couple of pages I have listed all the ways in which the recognition of these distortions and self-protective tendencies (defense mechanisms) can be exposed and addressed in group therapy, which is why it is such an essential and effective tool for chemical addictions. First though, let's take a look at all the interventions a therapist may employ in group psychotherapy.

FOCUS OF INTERVENTIONS

- Draw attention to thoughts, feelings, and behaviors
- Draw attention to the uniqueness of everyone
- Draw attention to the impact of addiction on one's self-concept

- Draw attention to victimization, especially in regards to use
- Draw attention to negative self-statements
- Draw attention to feelings of guilt, shame, and anger
- Explore one's need to control, emphasizing what they cannot control
- Help clients identify positive attributes of self [validation]
- Draw attention to the value of forgiveness for self and others
- Draw attention to discrepancies in the clients' life stories
- Draw attention to <u>healthy</u> and <u>unhealthy</u> defense mechanisms

(Taylor, 2008)

HEALTHY DEFENSE MECHANISMS

1. **Altruism** – do something for others without any expectation in return
2. **Humor** – laugh at inconveniences, accept obstacles as challenges
3. **Sublimation** – turn negative emotions into positive action
4. **Suppression** – temporarily setting emotion aside to deal with present
5. **Identification** – model characteristics you admire in others
6. **Introjection** – create and stick to your own set of personal values
7. **Anticipation** – create things to look forward to e.g., making vacation plans, or setting goals

(Taylor, 2008)

UNHEALTHY DEFENSE MECHANISMS

1. **Denial** – refusal to accept external reality because it's threatening
2. **Distortion** – gross reshaping of reality to meet own needs
3. **Delusional Projection** – grossly frank delusions of persecution
4. **Fantasy** – using fantasy to resolve inner and outer conflicts
5. **Projection** – expression onto others, i.e. prejudice, jealousy, injustice talk
6. **Hypochondria** – shifting negative feelings toward others onto self, e.g., illness
7. **Passive aggression** – e.g., sarcasm
8. **Acting out** – unconscious expression of emotion in behavior
9. **Displacement** – shifting sexual or aggressive impulses to a safer outlet
10. **Dissociation** – drastic modification of identity/character to avoid stress
11. **Intellectualization** – avoiding emotions by focusing on specifics
12. **Reaction Formation** – opposite behavior or belief to avoid anxiety
13. **Repression** – Pushing thoughts into the unconscious, but still feeling them

(Taylor, 2008)

TREATMENT APPROACHES

I have included an example of my STAALD approach to bring attention to the importance of having a guide to follow in the administration of treatment. All too often, clients are encouraged to accept their condition way before they even know what it is, and as you can see by this approach, *acceptance* (4) would not be sought after until all three of the previous goals are taught and/or met: First, of course, would be to (1) stop using. This would be detoxification and may include hospitalization. Next (2) would be to learn about the tools useful in remaining abstinent. And thirdly (3), is to help the patient gain awareness about the condition of addiction – so it can become possible for them to accept and address.

TREATMENT APPROACH

STAALD Approach (Provides Focus – an order to Interventions)
1. Stop using – Complete abstinence, chemical deprivation and slow return (Detox - Withdrawal)
2. Triggers – Address emotions, depression, people, places and things **(Recovery Tools)**
3. Awareness–Teach what addiction is through education, not pain or blame **(Knowledge)**
4. Acceptance - Encourage ownership of condition and responsible action **(Making a Decision)**

STAALD Approach (Provides Focus – an order to Interventions)

5. Learn– Assist in self-learning, model self-disclosure and group norms **(Group Therapy)**
    a. Encourage the practice of truth, honesty, humility, and usefulness – Authenticity
    b. Examine and address emotional pain, victimization, and psychosocial issues
    c. Unlearn egoistic/negative patterns of thinking & replace with positive ones
    d. Address cognitive distortions, defense mechanisms, & cognitive dissonance
    e. Assist in re-establishing or developing personal values – Self-esteem
    f. Encourage responsible behavior to build esteem and address self-betrayal – Integrity
    g. Encourage new interests and establishing goals – Case Management
    h. Encourage living in the present – relieves fear of the future and pain of the past
    i. Encourage healthy relationship with self, others, and world – Self-actualization

6. Devote – Self to enjoyment & improvement – Groups & Activities **(Discharge plan)**

As you can see, the first thing to do is to stop using. This is where one can be taught why they are not feeling okay and what to expect. Some may need medications, which can be very helpful in early recovery. Then they need to be taught some tools in order to avoid relapse and to address all the feelings they are likely to be experiencing and why, like depression, which is not only likely, but expected. Would you not be depressed if you just lost your best friend? They need to know what to expect so they will be better prepared to cope with these feelings. Thirdly they need to be taught what addiction is so they know what it is they have to fight, if they so choose. They must clearly understand that abstinence is not recovery.

This is where motivational interviewing and other techniques may be useful. It is only after all three of these goals have been accomplished that we can expect anyone to accept their condition and make a personal decision to seek recovery and start the recovery process.

If an addict wants to quit using just to please someone else or to get something back, this is not likely to last. To quit using and to recover are two entirely different goals. To seek recovery is a most personal decision which can only be made by the individual. And, in order to make this decision, they need to know what addiction is and how it has impacted them. Otherwise, they will not know what to believe, and therefore, cannot make a sincere decision. Recovery is all about psycho-emotional repair and healing, which can only be addressed after cessation (stopping).

STAGES OF RECOVERY

The stages of recovery are important to know because they can give the client and counselor an idea of which phase of the treatment any particular client is ready for. As I have previously demonstrated, knowing the stages of recovery that an addict must go through are very important. This is because it provides another guide in which to apply various therapeutic techniques. Prochaska & DiCemente's *Stages of Change* can be applied to every stage along the way, including termination. Recovery is a journey that takes time and it may help to know that it can take 1-3 years, or more, to progress through all these stages of recovery.

Recovery does not occur overnight, but it helps to know that it can and does end. Addicts do not need to be "in-recovery" forever!

LAD-CARE – Stages of Recovery

L-earning – involves learning about addiction and developing willingness/an open-mind: *requires surrendering* to the possibility of being ill (being different)

A-cceptance – involves dealing with the what and why of addiction/and the implications involved: *requires knowing* what they need to accept (a real tangible condition)

D-ecision – to stop using involves addressing ambivalence, self-worth, self-efficacy, visualization, hope, fear, etc.: *requires a belief* in own abilities to overcome addiction

C-ommitment – involves coping strategies, stress & time management, encouragement, action: *requires faith* in sobriety as offering a better way of life

A-cquirement – involves learning about self, feelings, perceptions, introspection, truth, insight, growth: *requires new relationship* with self, others, and the world

R-ecovery – involves continuous conscious effort in practicing a new way of thinking and behaving: *requires an unconditional acceptance* of condition

E-xaltation – involves the realization of being recovered: *requires a good deal of personal growth* with no intermittent desire-to-use. Maybe a thought every once in a while, but definitely no serious consideration or real desire

The reason I presented these guides for treatment here is because they are rarely, if ever, applied in treatment. *This is the essence of individualized treatment for addiction;* meeting clients where they are at in terms of how severe their addiction is and what they may need at each stage or level of recovery. That is to say: which interventions may be most useful or needed at one's individual degree of addiction. The same applies to each person's stage of, or progress in recovery. Through a continual assessment of each person's progress in recovery, more direct and efficient treatment interventions could be applied on an individual basis. This is meeting the treatment needs of the individual at their own specific degree of severity and/or stage of recovery.

However, because of the overwhelming influence of the psychosocial perspective, this concept of individualized treatment has taken on *a whole different meaning* – seeking to identify and address all that is believed to be the person's causal reasons for using; such as: family and relationship problems, mental health issues, unresolved trauma, unaddressed medical needs, problems with employment, and the lack of sober social support. This approach follows the assumption that if all these struggles (most of which are external consequences of addiction), were remedied, the addictive behavior would miraculously cease; thus, comes the premise: stop behavior = stop addiction (as presented in the Behavior vs. Condition chart). This approach, although attentive to individual needs, *is not individualized treatment for addiction.* We can do much better.

The person who relapses after two years of abstinence does not need the same amount or degree of treatment as the person who has never received treatment before. Nor does the person early in the progression of addiction need as much treatment as the person who has been severely affected by it for many years. In other words, we need to take the focus of treatment off the person (being the cause of their addiction) and put it on what each person may need on an individual basis; teaching them about the illness, the *condition of addiction*, and how to overcome the many internal psychosocial repercussions of addictive use that serve to keep the addiction alive. In this way, treatment can become much more efficient and effective in the future.

AXIOM –
"A statement accepted
as true, as basis for
argument or inference"
– Merriam-Webster (2000)

Chapter 14

Application

Hopefully, I have provided enough justification for the re-evaluation of our currently held causational perceptions and how they impact treatment, but what is the purpose of it all? The purpose is to implement a new perception of chemical addictions – a perception rooted in science and more beneficial to the population being served, not only in the treatment of addictions, but in the prevention of them as well. And, because an *accurate* depiction of biological vulnerability has not been fully accepted or applied in the field, we really only have the subjective and undocumented evidence of Alcoholics Anonymous (AA) to predict any level of improvement, if any at all. Therefore, in considering how poorly the psychosocial perspective has been working up to this point, with an estimated 1-2% success rate for first-timers in treatment, what do we really have to lose by trying something different? Why not try something based on research rather than the fallibility of human logic?

The biological perspective of causation is not about releasing people from the responsibility of their behavior (which is a very real concern). It is about encouraging people to take responsibility for their condition. If the success of AA is any indication of how well this perspective can work, this concern is unjustified. In my experience, the biological perspective actually helps motivate people with addictions to stick with abstinence. It is through this perspective that addicts can finally realize why they could never learn to control their use no matter how hard they might have tried. It explains to them why they could have so much will-power in other areas of their life yet be rendered powerless when it came to controlling their use. This is why the biological perspective has the potential to be much more effective. To the normal drinker and occasional drug user, this "powerless" aspect of addiction may sound a bit ridiculous, but to the person with an addiction it makes perfectly good sense. This is why it is important to educate not only the addict, but their family and close loved ones as well. Otherwise they cannot understand why their loved one just won't quit (as they believe they themselves would do).

This biological perspective may be quite hard for family and friends of those afflicted to accept, and it may be just as hard for many treatment providers as well (to say nothing of their willingness to teach and apply). Since we are talking about beliefs here, this change is going to be hard to implement. It cannot take place on an administrative level alone, although it would help; it must occur on an individual basis with treatment providers if it is going to take hold and be effective.

EXTERNAL EXCUSES

Insinuations, suggestions, or outright blaming an addiction on a person's life-course experiences and events (e.g., divorce, death, trauma, physical and sexual abuse, poverty, etc.) may be the most detrimental practice currently being used. It is this kind of thinking that encourages addicts to place the blame of their addiction on others and their life-course circumstances. In blaming addiction on others or any past hardship, it makes it all too easy for addicts to avoid taking responsibility for the condition they have. This is why they need to learn that their addiction is caused by their biological reaction, and they need to accept the responsibility for having this condition.

When discussing psychosocial issues with patients it can be very tempting to let them believe their problems caused them to overindulge in drug use and therefore caused their addiction, but this will not help them. It will actually make their struggle much harder. This is why they should be informed that these issues *only* played a role in the development, progression, and maintenance of their addiction *because* of their biologic reaction to the drug. All the various psychosocial issues that help drive an addiction must of course be addressed because they contribute heavily to using, but to refer to them as causation is a mistake.

Also, to passively allow clients to think their problems caused them to become addicted is just as much of an injustice, because we have evidence to the contrary. The best way to explain the role that psychosocial issues play in the development of addiction is to explain that they only contribute to use, they do not cause it. Addicts must understand that most people who drink or use psychotropic substances to cope with traumatic experiences or problems in life, usually never become addicted. It is only those with a fairly high biological reaction to a substance that do. This explains why they may have turned to the use of a substance to cope with their problems in life but without placing blame. In other words, the drug might have saved them before it turned on them; they may have found plenty of comfort in a drug at a time when they needed it the most. It is quite normal for biologically vulnerable people to handle or cope with psychosocial problems (or memories of these problems) by using. Non-addicts also over-indulge in using during times of hardship but they do not become addicts because of it. This is because non-addicts do not receive the same biological effects (intensities & loss of control) or adaptations (neurological changes) from the drug as addicts do. Becoming aware of these differences will help those in treatment immensely, because it will help them learn to accept their condition.

According to this biological perspective (of the bio-psycho-social model of addiction), the drug-of-addiction will pick away at the emotional regulatory structures of the brain in those who are vulnerable to this type of *adaptation* well before they lose all control of their frequency of use. Adaptation is only one aspect of bio-vulnerability. Different degrees of *effect* that a drug can have on the individual, such as losing all control of consumption when using, is the other aspect of bio-vulnerability. This can speed up the process of bio-adaptation in those who are more vulnerable to neurological *adaptations* (the increase/decrease of receptor sites).

I have met addicts who can go days and even months without using, only to lose all control of their consumption when they do use; conversely, I have met addicts that cannot even make it through one day without using. This may be the culmination of both psychological and biological adaptations, but make no mistake, both are addiction. Both are abnormal responses to the use of a substance. And because of the progression, which is likely to be a slow decline of normal neurological functioning caused by the drug, the person who experiences complete loss-of-control over their consumption will be more likely to reach the point of daily use eventually, with or without the added stress placed upon the brain's circuitry by traumatic experiences.

This is why addicts must be purposely informed that the drug caused their addiction, reminding them that not everyone who experiences problems in life become addicts. They must learn to put the blame where it belongs, on the drug. The facts are: (1) drugs cause addiction only in people who are susceptible to them; and, (2) most of those who try, or even use drugs on a regular basis, never become addicts. These are two facts we cannot continue to ignore in treatment any longer. In order to avoid any further confusion or misapplication of the biological perspective (different degrees of effects and adaptations) it is important to be aware of how this biological perspective has been misinterpreted and misapplied by providers coming from a more psychosocial causal belief. Since both perspectives are included in the categorical term of "Biopsychosocial Model of Addiction," this can be confusing.

PSYCHOSOCIAL & BIOLOGICAL PERSPECTIVES

According to the <u>biological perspective</u>, as we have learned through science, the drug causes addiction only in people for whom the drug can produce higher degrees of effect and/or adaptations, thereby disrupting normal brain functioning and leading to a plethora of mental health problems and developmental delays. Once abstinent and recovered, the addict is as "normal" as anyone else.

According to the <u>psychosocial perspective</u>, biological vulnerability is interpreted as inferior mental abilities due to genetic factors, such as high impulsivity and/or poor decision making skills that account for the addict's inability to control their use. And, even if they do succeed in obtaining abstinence, they will never be quite as "normal" as others. They will always remain at risk for relapse because of these deficiencies (or damage). Thus, the best they can hope for is to be "in-recovery" for the rest of their life, as long as they maintain a recovery program.

There are other reasons why this axiom of having to be in-recovery forever has taken such a firm hold in the field (such as to explain away relapse) but this is not what is important here. What is important to understand is how the meaning of biological vulnerability has been misinterpreted in an attempt to fit bio-vulnerability into the old, and well-established beliefs of the psychosocial perspective. By knowing this, we can avoid this trap. This is not what our evidence has provided. In fact, there is no scientific evidence to support this psychosocial interpretation of biological vulnerability in regards to causation.

The other misrepresentation of biological vulnerability has more to do with the selective use of information. This happens when addicts are only informed about adaptations (damage), and told nothing about the varying degrees of resistance to adaptation (and nothing about the varying degrees of effects either). This can leave addicts blaming themselves, which may actually be the intent behind this selective use of information. They may need this information; however, they must also be informed that these changes do not occur, or at least not at the same rate, in everyone who uses alcohol or drugs. This practice of only telling one side of the story appears to stem from the myth that drugs affect every human being exactly the same. It is based on the belief that anyone could become addicted to a psychotropic substance if they just used enough and more so if they experience specific psychosocial circumstances in their life; those so called "risk-factors" that we have already discussed.

Again, there is no solid evidence to support this belief that anyone could become addicted. In fact, the evidence firmly contradicts this assumption. There are just too many people in the world who do not receive enough pleasure from the effects of a psychotropic substance for this assumption to hold any weight. Different people receive different degrees of effect from the same drugs. In fact, some people react adversely to the same drugs others get addicted to, and therefore would never use the drug on a continual basis. Despite the fact that drugs affect everyone slightly differently, many professionals still insist everyone has the same chance of becoming addicted to any substance, given just the right psychosocial circumstances. These professionals claim that it is only through self-control and situational fate that most people do not. It is this type of thinking that needs correction, especially in the field of treatment.

Coping with problems by using a chemical substance does not make an addict. Physicians have been prescribing psychotropic drugs for this very same purpose for decades, to which most patients (*not all*) never become addicted.

When applying the biological part of the Biopsychosocial Model of Addiction clearly and in its entirety, without distortion or bias, it forces the addict to take responsibility for having the condition they have, not for causing it.

FAITH

Developing a sound belief in one's ability to fully recover is essential for making progress in treatment. Clients need to envision themselves as happy, healthy individuals in sobriety, or recovery will be next to impossible. This is why perspectives are so vitally important, especially when it comes to what is portrayed in treatment. One perspective tears the addict down while the other builds them up. This is why the biological perspective, the latter of these two, is much easier for the addict to accept. This means recovery is likely to be achieved much sooner, and with less recurring treatment attempts. It also provides the hope of complete recovery, which is the difference between hoping for maintenance versus obtaining recovery once and for all. This is important:

The psychosocial causal perspective promotes a <u>conditional recovery</u> based upon one's level of mental and emotional health; whereas, the biological perspective promotes an <u>unconditional recovery</u> based upon a firm acceptance of one's own individual biological reaction.

This is why the biological perspective promises to be much more effective. There is nothing anyone can do to change their degree or level of *biological susceptibility*. Therefore, the addict's only recourse is to accept their condition and learn to be happy living a sober life; which if obtained, is being "recovered." This does not mean one cannot reactivate their addiction at any time in the future. There are no guarantees for either type of recovery. The difference here is that it is much harder for one to all of a sudden disbelieve how their drug affects them, especially if they slip a few times, versus how easy it can be for one to start thinking they are mentally and emotionally healthy enough to start using again.

In order to guide patients toward a strong recovery, they must be informed that their addiction was not of their own making or a response to their life-course experiences. To do this, I would suggest starting each group or session with a few simple questions, such as: (1) "What is addiction?" The answer I would be looking for here is, "My desire-to-use," or, "My want-to-use." This answer personalizes the addiction and helps the patient recognize the condition they have within. It is the tangible part of addiction because all addicts know the gut-wrenching feeling behind their desire-to-use and the persistent mental obsession to satisfy it. In time these questions and answers are likely to become automatic acknowledgements of their condition. From them they will learn what it is they have to battle. The second question I would suggest using is, (2) "What causes addiction?" The answer I would be seeking in this one would be, "Drugs cause addiction." This is obvious, and it can be quite annoying for those in treatment to have to hear it all the time, but this is also why they will never forget it. Then occasionally I would ask, (3) "Do drugs cause addiction in everyone?" The answer I would be seeking here would be, "No – Drugs affect people differently." This question addresses the occasional doubts they are very likely to have. Repeating these questions over and over again (as simple and silly as this may sound) helps clients to build a solid *belief* on which to build their recovery. It provides them with an unconditional foundation.

Doing this is merely making use of the facts and reinforcing them. If treatment providers do not believe in these statements, it is very unlikely their clients will either. Let me reiterate one more point; this is a solid foundation because it is based on science, and it is unconditional. With the acceptance of one's biological reaction there is no possibility of ever using safely, and this needs to be reinforced by the provider if we are ever going to stop the revolving door of treatment.

This is an explicitly direct approach that does not confuse those in treatment. The use of repetition is not very different than the subtle insinuations that consistently reinforce the psychosocial perspective (e.g., what is your drug of choice?), which are not based on facts but on theoretical beliefs; and for the most part are very confusing because they are delivered so implicitly.

Chemical addictions resemble many definitions of disease and therefore have been referred to as such, a chronic disease; however, since the desire-to-use (the addiction) is not permanent (the only permanence is the response to use - the reaction), it is inaccurate to label addiction as a chronic disease. In my opinion, a more accurate definition would place chemical addictions under its very own medical definition; such as, "a chemical reaction," which is what it actually is. It is an idiosyncratic response to a drug that calls for more use and has a life of its own - which can result in premature death if left untreated. It is a hypersensitivity to a specific chemical substance.

Using the "chemically induced" distinction is very important because it separates chemical addictions from all the obsessive compulsive disorders (OCDs) that are so often called addictions today (e.g., gambling, sex, shopping, eating, etc.). Using the word addiction with these disorders distorts the truth, as they imply that they are no different from chemical addictions; that chemical addictions are just another obsessive compulsion. This is very likely to be a direct result of the psychosocial perspective, which ignores the fact that chemical addictions are a real biological condition. This is why clients must be made aware of the difference between chemical addictions and so-called process addictions. If chemical addictions were mere obsessive compulsions, then of course, addicts could learn to keep their compulsion to use in check without having to give it up completely. This is why it is dangerous to allow addicts to think that their condition is, or the result of, an obsessive compulsion. Because of the condition itself, the absolute love for the effects of a drug, addicts will jump on any explanation that gives them hope of using again someday.

TERMINOLOGY

Applying the biological perspective, while at the same time using some common terms and phrases in the field that support the psychosocial perspective can be very confusing to clients and hinder their recovery. Some of these have become so commonly used that one may not easily recognize the implications behind them. One of these is "drug of choice." This obviously insinuates that the addict "chooses" to use their drug. Taking this a bit further, an addict may internalize this phrase as the professional telling them that they are guilty for causing their addiction because they chose to use. They may or may not be consciously aware of this insinuation, but the message is likely to be internalized just the same. This saying appears to have originated out of the well-accepted theory that all behavior is learned (psychosocial); and if addiction was the result of poor behavior, it would be most fitting. However, we now know that this is not the case, and to imply that it is only provides confusion and reinforces the guilt, shame, and blame associated with the assumption of having a choice.

Also, knowing that behavior is learned, it is very easy to conclude that it can be unlearned as well. If this is what is being taught, addicts will inevitably try to teach themselves to control and moderate their use, which sounds most reasonable, even if they are informed of the likelihood of having a damaged brain. Remember, they absolutely love their drug. To combat this response under the psychosocial perspective, addicts are expected to accept the self-imposed consequences of their use (damage they did to their brains) as an explanation for why they can never use safely ever again. In all practicality, this just imposes more shame and guilt. As you can see one little saying (drug of choice) can imply so very much. The use of this phrase obviously contradicts the biological perspective (effects and adaptations) and is very likely to contribute to the confusion most addicts have in regards to what addiction is and where it stems from. Therefore, using the terms, "drug of addiction" or "drug of use" is more appropriate.

Another term that is highly contradictory to the biological perspective is the term "in-recovery." This term is fine for people in treatment, because this is where they are at when they are in treatment. When this term is used to refer to any person who has recovered from an addiction, it is demeaning and minimizes their accomplishment. Who would want to strive for that? This is a terrible and hopeless message to be sending to those in treatment. It clearly sends the message that there is no end to recovery, which is an outright fabrication.

People were not meant to consume chemicals, and just because most people can (without much or any harm), does not mean that there is anything wrong with those who cannot.

Addiction is not a dysfunction, or a permanent mental inadequacy that one must live with and treat for the rest of their lives, as the use of the term in-recovery clearly implies. I most earnestly recommend the discontinuance of this term when referring to those who have won the battle of addiction; for they are actually heroes who deserve the same degree of respect freely granted to those who have overcome other life-threatening illnesses. It is time we give them the respect they deserve. Just because one is susceptible to a specific drug's effects and adaptations, having the condition of addiction (being vulnerable), does not mean recovered addicts are ill forever.

Certainly the use of this term, in-recovery, was meant well; to remind patients they need to remain vigilant, but it serves treatment providers much more than it serves patients. Under this way of thinking about recovery, as a need for endless maintenance, if a client relapses, then their relapse is not due to any lack of treatment efforts or expertise, it is due to the patient's failure in maintaining their recovery – thus, again, the blame is placed right back on the patient.

Where the use of some terms can hinder treatment so can the avoidance of some more appropriate terms. Many providers profess that the use of the word addict is inappropriate. They think the use of this word is disrespectful, that it defines the person as their condition and that it fuels the stigma of addiction. Obviously, since I have been using this word throughout, as a reference to those with addictions, I totally disagree. Addiction must be addressed head-on, and *those who have the condition of addiction must talk it to death*. Any avoidance only serves as a distraction from the acceptance of the condition, which one must take responsibility for having. There is no room in treatment for any avoidance. There is absolutely no difference between referring to a person with an addiction as an addict and referring to them as a chemically dependent person, as they both share the same meaning. It is just easier and faster to convey this information by using the word addict.

The appropriate use of the word addict is not disrespectful at all. It really has nothing to do with the stigma of addiction, for it only defines a *condition*. The stigma lies in the misconception of what *causes* addiction, and it no more defines a person as only being an addict any more than referring to a person with diabetes as only being a diabetic. We obviously know diabetics are much more than their condition, just as we know addicts are much more than their condition. Because of this, avoiding the use of this term, *only for addicts*, I might add, actually fuels the stigma. *A person is an addict when they are addicted – when they possess the desire to use.* When they recover, they are no longer an addict – they are just a person who cannot use illicit or recreational drugs like other people, and there is nothing wrong with that!

Just like the *use* of the term "in-recovery" stands to benefit the provider more than the patient, the *avoidance* of the word addict might do the same. It may just be that the use of the word addict exposes the counselors' true causational beliefs, for they are the ones connecting the word addict to the stigma behind it. Remember, stigma is all about self-causation. Therefore, the recent movement to expel the use of this word, under the guise of easing shame and guilt for the client, may just be an attempt to ease the provider's guilt when they use this word; for most of them actually do believe clients play a huge part in causing their own addictions.

For the addict, avoiding the use of the word addict can allow for the avoidance of acceptance – the acceptance of their condition; which, as you may know by now is a requirement for making any real progress in treatment. This is the fourth goal of the STAALD approach. Actually, the use of the words addict and alcoholic can be very useful. For example, every time an alcoholic speaks up in an AA meeting they introduce themselves like this, "My name is such and such, and I am an alcoholic." In making this declaration, they are not disrespecting themselves; quite the contrary. What they are actually saying is, "My name is such and such, and I have the "allergic" reaction to alcohol (bio-vulnerability)." In AA, this practice serves as a constant reminder of their condition; that their powerlessness over alcohol is the knowledge of what alcohol can and will always do to them. Acknowledging one's powerlessness in the 1st step is the acknowledgement of their "allergic" reaction. This is actually a very wise, healthy and useful practice. It is a recovery tool, something all addicts can benefit from.

Another detrimental practice of avoidance has to do with the discouragement of disclosure of previous addictions. Counselors who have overcome an addiction are an invaluable source of knowledge, not only for those who are in treatment but also for any treatment agency. They possess knowledge that other counselors can learn from, and they can relate to those in treatment; however, their real value may lie in being a living example of health in recovery; a recovery that bears no shame or guilt. I have already discussed how powerful the ability to relate can be in my reference to *The Power of Words* video, so I will not go into depth here. But I think it is important to highlight some of the problems associated with counselor non-disclosure, and how effective it can be for clients to witness recovery first hand, (*when addiction is viewed as nobody's fault*); something the biological perspective promotes.

The two major problems with non-disclosure are (1) it is deceitful and addicts can see right through it – as it models secrecy – something that is very detrimental to recovery because it contradicts the addict's need to be open and honest; and (2), it contributes to the stigma of addiction by the way this secrecy implies that there is definitely something to hide about having had an addiction – either some kind of fault or dysfunction. Clients in treatment may or may not know they are taking all this in, but nevertheless, the message is loud and clear; this is what they are taking in through non-disclosure, addiction is something to be ashamed of. And this, of course, would be true if addicts were actually mentally deficient or responsible for causing their own addictions. Either way, the prohibition of counselor self-disclosure is a "lose-lose" situation for both the addict and counselor.

Conversely, open-disclosure sends just the opposite the message: that there is absolutely nothing wrong with people who have overcome the chronic life-threatening condition of addiction. Counselors who disclose whether or not they have ever had and addiction in the past are likely to earn the respect of their clients as well. There is nothing wrong with telling the truth and letting clients teach us what it is like to have an addiction, for they are the experts in what it is like for them. In the process, they will be learning to identify their addiction within. So you see, self-disclosure is a "win-win" situation for all of us. Not only does it support the fact that addicts are not responsible for causing their addictions, but it supports the evidence we have to share with them. The evidence they need to be aware of in order to gain the belief that will benefit them; the belief that they cannot, and never could use safely.

Supporters of non-disclosure promote this practice of undue secrecy as being a matter of maintaining boundaries, which is something all professionals need to be aware of. However, when counselor self-disclosure is limited to the thoughts and feelings associated with addiction, it has nothing to do with violating boundaries; or even taking the focus off the client, which is another defense for non-disclosure. In support of counselors who can (and should) disclose a previous addiction, I must reiterate, counselor disclosure should not include story-telling. The mere fact that they have recovered *and are not ashamed of having had an addiction* is sufficient enough. In this way, no addict can compare themselves out of treatment. In the future, as the use of our biological evidence becomes more and more accepted counselor self-disclosure will be encouraged and clients will be able to see that having an addiction is no worse or better than any other illness. They will know it is no different than any number of conditions/diseases that derive from higher levels of biological vulnerability (e.g., diabetes, skin cancer, heart disease, celiac disease, etc.).

Counselor self-disclosure must also accompany the proper *application of the biological perspective;* otherwise, it will be of no real value to those being served. It would just be a display of repentance and the acceptance of all the guilt and shame currently associated with addiction, which only serves to hinder one's acceptance of the condition. Therefore, with the acceptance of this new biological perspective, not only will we be able to take advantage of this most valuable resource, self-disclosure, but we may just start to see some significant improvements in treatment effectiveness as well.

CHALLENGE –
"To dispute - especially
as being unjust, invalid,
or outmoded"
– Merriam-Webster (2000)

Chapter 15

The Challenge

In preparing this book for publication, the thought occurred to me that I should present my readers with a challenge. Would they get the full implication of what I have presented? Would they understand what I meant by referring to addicts as "those less fortunate?" Well, here it is in a nutshell:

If you think you have kept yourself from becoming an addict or alcoholic by making better choices in life – then you have missed something and I have failed to convey a thorough understanding.

I realize how dramatic this may sound, but if your ego is hurt by this statement, then I have not accomplished my objective. I have not conveyed to you a clear, concise, and comprehensive understanding of addiction. Therefore, in one last ditch effort, I have decided to elaborate on some very important points.

Unless one *believes* they are biologically vulnerable to addiction, they cannot, or would not, make a conscious effort to avoid it. One will not fight off their desire-to-use unless they believe it could happen to them. And, as long as one thinks they are in control, as all vulnerable and non-vulnerable people do, they are not very likely to deprive themselves of such an extremely pleasurable experience; a pleasure that may actually be much more damaging for some than others, especially when they see others using the same substances without consequence. The fact of the matter is, non-addicts have the ability to control their desire-to-use and those who are more vulnerable have less of this ability. This is because of what the drug does to them — their intense reactions. They may not be physically addicted from the start, but since the effects are stronger on some people than others, as the evidence suggests, to not use would be like going against their most natural instincts. Kind of like denying themselves food or water for no apparent reason, and this is the clincher; addicts do not see any reason why they should deny themselves such a pleasure, especially when they see others using the same substances. They are oblivious to the fact that they may be receiving much stronger and more damaging effects from the substance than those around them. Like you and I, they have been taught, through various social networks, that all they have to do is control their use. For they believe they are just as much in control of their use as anyone else — they are completely unaware of their vulnerability.

I am not saying that one cannot avoid a chemical addiction by making the choice not to use. Theoretically, this statement is true, for it is always the drug that causes addiction, not the person – it's just that in reality they won't, especially if they are receiving intense pleasure from a substance. In other words, there is no reason for them to make a decision not to use a substance, and deny themselves such a pleasure without the knowledge that they themselves *could* and *would* become addicted. This is how millions of people avoid an addiction to heroin, for they know it is one of the most addictive substances out there. They fear it would take hold of them. Therefore, if you don't try a drug, you cannot become addicted to it, but this is not reality when it comes to drugs of social acceptance. There are many other substances that are less feared, and this is where most all addictions start.

Genes alone will not determine whether or not a person will develop an addiction. There are three factors involved in the development of addiction and they all exist on a continuum from low to high vulnerability. What I am saying is that unless one knows how vulnerable they are to the effects of a specific drug, and then makes a conscious effort to avoid the use of that drug, addiction will be inevitable. It will run its natural course and develop in response to the drug's effects, which is to seek its use for the extreme pleasure, or relief, it can provide, specifically for those more impacted by the drug – those who are more biologically vulnerable.

For those who believe they have kept themselves from developing an addiction, they must learn that they themselves are not as vulnerable to a particular substance as those who do become addicted. This is not easy to comprehend, so let me share a quick little story that exemplifies the reality of genetic predisposition:

Once upon a time, there was a teenage boy who wanted to try some alcohol, so he challenged a friend to drink with him. This friend did not want to try the alcohol, but after failing in an attempt to persuade the boy out of it, he gave into the challenge. Both were healthy well-adjusted boys from good families and both drank three shots of liquor from a new quart bottle. Within 15 minutes the boy who wanted to try the alcohol did not feel well and went home. On the other hand, the friend who did not want to try the alcohol was so impacted by the effects of it he ended up drinking the rest of the bottle all by himself. At some point he blacked out and did not recall finishing the bottle. It was as though the alcohol had a mind of its own – the reaction was to drink more and more – and this went on for the next twenty years. The boy who wanted to try the alcohol in the first place, and who did not like the effects, eventually learned to drink like a gentleman. Now a man, this gentleman stands in judgment of his friend, the drunk. This is a true story.

This story is a prime example of genetic predisposition; that one's reaction to a substance is completely out of one's control. However, beliefs also play a major role in the development of addiction as well. If a biologically vulnerable person believes they are not vulnerable, as most all do and continue using despite having very intense reactions, high tolerance, or losing all control of their consumption when using, they are unwittingly setting themselves up for addiction. This happens a lot in societies where partying is valued as a socially accepted recreational activity, especially among young men. For them, having the ability to consume large amounts of a substance is admired and actually sought after for respect. The real culprit in this is that all people, both vulnerable and non-vulnerable, believe they possess the common sense and fortitude to keep them from ever becoming an addict. This belief is especially dangerous for those who are more vulnerable because not only do they appear to be able to withstand greater amounts of a substance, they also possess a greater desire or need to keep on using.

As I mentioned, there are many people who keep themselves from becoming addicted to heroin only because of their fear of it; the fear that they would become addicted if they did try it – thus, they *believed* in the power of what *the drug* could do to them, personally! Without a belief in what a drug can do, addiction is inevitable; it may only be inevitable for those who are biologically vulnerable to a particular substance, but nobody (at this point in time) can know this until it is too late, until the addiction is firmly set and enough consequences have occurred to make it virtually impossible to ignore. This is why no one can prevent a chemical addiction. They must first *believe* they are vulnerable to addiction in order to make a conscious and sincere effort to avoid it. And, nobody really does this, especially not those who are receiving an overwhelming sensation from the substance.

This is the problem: nobody knows how vulnerable they are to a specific substance until after they have developed an addiction. Identifying one's own susceptibility is hard for people, especially when they see others using the same substance with impunity. This is compounded by the fact that more biologically vulnerable people receive greater degrees of effects when using. The individual differences here lie not only in how powerful the drug is on the individual brain, but also in how psychosocially impacted they are by the drug as well – how much they love and desire the effects – their genetically determined and unknown degrees of bio-psycho-social vulnerabilities, such as I presented in the biopsychosocial matrix. Drug use affects all areas of a person's life. Without the knowledge or fear of what the drug can do to them personally and the lack of *belief* in one's own level of biological vulnerability, the development of addiction is virtually unavoidable.

This is why no one can rightfully claim that they have kept themselves from developing an addiction – the effects are such that highly vulnerable people will return to them, especially if they believe that they themselves could never become addicted, for they would never let themselves. You see, they believe they are in control just like everyone else. The only people that can rightfully claim that they have kept themselves from becoming an addict and actually own it, are the ones who refused to try a substance in the first place. And since nearly everyone in a developed society has tried an addictive substance, none of these people can claim that they have intentionally kept themselves from becoming an addict.

Biologic vulnerability is beyond a person's ability to control or alter and there are plenty of other elements that lay beyond a person's control as well, such as the environment in which one was raised, the culturally accepted using norms and expectations of the society in which they reside, and one's acquired attitudes toward using because of other psychosocial influences, such as being raised by parents who drink and use drugs. These are all things that no one has any control over, and unless we come to acknowledge and accept these realities we will not be in a very good position to be of assistance to those in need. If there was any way for an addict to arrest and stop their addiction before it came to the point of needing treatment, they would have taken it. In this way, both addicts and non-addicts are exactly alike. They are both human, and one thing all humans have in common is the need to have control over their own actions. The main reason they do not take action before it is too late lies in the false belief that they do have control over their use, as they see other people doing.

The addict thinks of addiction the same way the world does; as a daily need to use a substance and the inability to stop using. This is not the case at all. All addicts have the ability to stop using when they are sober – they just do not have the ability to stay stopped. This is because, in reality, the brain has been altered and it is just too uncomfortable for them to deny themselves this pleasure or relief, for very long. This is why their *choice* to use has been taken away from them.

This gradual loss of choice is a very important concept to understand. This is how the drug slowly takes over one's mind and body in those who are biologically vulnerable. As they believe they are in control, as all people do, the drug is slowly altering the core structures of the brain leaving the vulnerable person (the host) dependent upon the drug's effects. And, over the course of time and exposure, while the drug is slowly altering the brain's need for the drug, the vulnerable person adapts both mentally and socially. Their whole life starts to evolve around the use of their drug. Therefore, what appears to be a poor choice to use, or that of a poor lifestyle, it is actually a response to the effects of the drug on all three biopsychosocial aspects of one's life. Remember the circular progression? With this process clearly understood, we can begin to understand that:

It is only through biological luck and situational fate that most people never develop a chemical addiction.

The effects drugs have on those who are more vulnerable are a lot like the effects of a deadly virus. For example, before we had a vaccine for tuberculosis, two people could come in contact with the virus, but only one of them might come down with the disease. This is where one person's immune system is more vulnerable to the virus than another. In the same way, instead of coming in contact with a deadly virus in the environment, "addicts-to-be" come in contact with a drug to which they are highly vulnerable. In one person the effects are so great they are bound to return to the drug (especially if neurotransmitter levels do not return to normal after use); whereas, in another person they might like the effects, but it may not produce the same degree of effects (or alter neuro-transmitter levels after use), which are evidently much stronger and more damaging for some people than others. We have evidence as to why this happens, which is that some people are more neurologically attracted to various substances than others through differences in neurological structure and activity. Therefore, the pull to return to the drug and use more would be greater in one person than another, such as in the results of Dr. Nora Volkow's dopamine type-2 (D2) stimulant experiment.

In addition to the different degrees of *effects* that people experience with various drugs, we also have some pretty strong evidence that some brains are more *resistant* to neurological adaptation than others. For those who develop addictions, physical changes occur to brain structures, such as whole neurons and chemical receptor sites dying off, as well as reuptake sites shutting down and growing additional receptor sites. Again, these biological adaptations do not occur at the same rate, even with the same amount of consumption in all people. In other words, most brains are just more resistant to these changes, and this has nothing to do with a person's thinking, attitude, or using behavior. Our lab experiments have confirmed this over and over, and not only in animal experiments, but in all the human brain imaging that has been done over the past couple of decades.

By now I hope you can see that addicts are really no different than non-addicts. The only real difference between the addict and non-addict is their individual levels of biological vulnerability to various substances. They both believe they can control their use and this is exactly why AA described alcoholism as cunning, baffling, and powerful; it sneaks up on normal people just like you and me long before they even know what hit them. The more vulnerable a person is to a psychotropic substance, the more loss-of-control over their consumption they will experience. This does not mean they have lost control over whether or not they use in the first place, but loss-of-control does appear to be one indication of higher vulnerability that does lead to full-blown addiction. That's why it's critical that bio-vulnerability becomes common knowledge, otherwise millions of unsuspecting people will continue to be sucked into the sneaky grip of addiction year after year, especially if they are hell bent on gaining control over their use - which of course, they are incapable of doing because of their biological reaction to the drug. This particular reaction has nothing to do with other psychosocial vulnerabilities. *A loss-of-control of consumption while under the influence of a drug is strictly a biological reaction.* We know this because of all the people who have overcome addictions and still cannot control their amount of consumption when they slip or relapse. This is what powerlessness is all about – it is the inability to change one's biological reaction to a substance, regardless of psychological health. One may be powerless over what a drug does to them, but they are not powerless over whether or not they use the drug. This must be clearly understood if one is going to overcome their addiction. It is also why chemical addictions are so very different from other so-called addictions.

This concept that *biological vulnerability underlies all chemical addictions* may be very hard to grasp, much less believe, but when it comes right down to it, the facts are the facts. Addiction is a "**BEAR**." It stems from **B**iological differences, with different degrees of **E**ffects, different degrees of **A**daptations, and different degrees of **R**esistance to change. To accept these facts, this truth, is very hard for some people. This is just as hard for the millions of recovered addicts who have already fallen prey to the *belief* that they had in some way caused their own addiction; and sadly for them, had to reach some great depths of despair in order to accept the psychosocial fallacy of self-causation. This is what the biological perspective can accomplish; it can raise the "bottoms" of all those caught in the grips of addiction. It is through the acceptance of this perspective that the afflicted can finally accept the reality of their biological fate.

If professionals can accept these facts and start to promote the use of our biological information, it will have a profound impact on the public's causal perceptions of addiction. Then, not only will we see less people in treatment – for some will be more willing to accept their biological fate and stop using on their own before it gets severe, but we will also be in a much better position to assist all those in need of help by indirectly preparing "addicts-to-be" for treatment. In this way we would be addressing the issue of denial and resistance on a large scale basis. Since our fellow brethren are the public, and they are the people who develop addictions, they are the ones who come into treatment with the public's stigmatized view of addiction, which is a huge barrier. Clearly, changing the public's view and opinion of addiction will be a big job; however, it is not impossible and a good place to start is within the profession.

Many excellent and well intentioned practitioners in the field have been led down the same path of believing that something or someone is ultimately responsible for addictions. For example, written in the DSM IV-TR Case Book (Volume 2), there is a case study of a patient who was ". . . refusing to blame his family for his difficulties" (Spitzer, et. al., 2006, p. 61) and was therefore *deemed resistant to therapy*. In other words, just because he would not accept his treatment provider's causational beliefs, this was the explanation given for why his treatment failed - sound familiar? In this case, the cause was assumed to be the members of his family instead of the patient. However, the point here is to recognize just how much blaming actually occurs, not only in treatment, but in the educational system as well. Most students have no idea how much they have been influenced by the causational beliefs of others long before they even graduate. In society, as well as in most treatment facilities and in thousands of text books for students, self-causal and situational beliefs about addiction abound. And we wonder why the stigma of addiction remains?

Gaining a full and complete understanding of addiction involves a synthesis of all the evidence, much like putting all the pieces of a puzzle together until eventually, a clearer and more comprehensive view of addiction comes into focus. This is what all our biological research and evidence has provided for us. It can help us make addiction more understandable and provide us with a better idea of where all the psychosocial factors fit in. In the process, we can begin to understand how all the other various psychosocial factors play into the <u>development</u> of addiction, what role they play in the <u>progression</u> of addiction, and what role they play in the <u>maintenance</u> of addiction. Then we can begin to see how they play a greater and greater role in the progression as the addiction gets worse and worse (remember the reciprocal action of Spiral Progression).

In a society that values the use of recreational substances, such as alcohol and marijuana, it is imperative that we start to acknowledge biological differences in people. Even with a high degree of biological vulnerability, other factors must also be involved for a chemical addiction to develop. So, one might ask, "Why not include all factors/causes, such as psycho-emotional, socio-environmental, as well as moral and spiritual factors? Surely all these factors are involved as well." True, they are all factors, but this is critically important: they are not all causes because:

Biological vulnerability is not an all-or-nothing condition.

It is about having a potential for addiction – that's all. Just because a person has a high degree of biological vulnerability does not mean that they are destined to develop an addiction. There is a big difference between the inheritance of a genetic *determinant* for a specific disease, such as sickle cell anemia, hemophilia, muscular dystrophy, cystic fibrosis, etc. (which, as far as we know, cannot be avoided) and the passing down of a genetic *vulnerability* to various diseases, such as: type-II diabetes, skin cancer, rheumatoid arthritis, and even addiction, which only passes down a potential for the disease/condition. With vulnerability, it's epigenetic. It takes something else in the environment or specific conditions to activate the disease or condition.

This "something else in the environment" would be (1) the drug-of-use the person is vulnerable to, and (2) something that creates a condition for using, such as: the effects of the substance being so intensely pleasurable the person is bound to return to it as often as possible (and especially if they lose all control over the amount of consumption while using); or it could be other specific conditions such as childhood trauma, psychological and emotional difficulties, families that model using, and even one's ability to access the substance. All these could increase one's amount of consumption and using frequency; and thus contribute highly to the development of addiction through increases in consumption.

Since biological vulnerability exists on a continuum, social-environmental and psychological factors are going to play a much greater role in the development of addiction for those with a moderate degree of bio-vulnerability than for those with either high or low degrees of bio-vulnerability. This explains why rates of alcoholism in countries were drunkenness is frowned upon is lower than in countries where drunkenness is more accepted. This can happen when more people with a moderate degree of bio-vulnerability (those closer to the middle of the bio-vulnerability continuum) consume more, and thus increase the overall rates of addiction in that country. This same concept applies to various populations within a country.

It is always the person's biological relationship to the drug that underlies all chemical addictions. Other environmental factors can both increase or decrease the rates of addiction by playing a greater role in those who could go either way – people who are moderately vulnerable to a substance. However, for those with extremely high degrees of biological vulnerability, it appears that these other psychosocial factors do not play as much of a role, even though some are likely to be present (e.g., access and availability). Therefore, the one and only true cause of addiction is the drug, even though all three biopsychosocial factors play a role in the development of chemical addictions. In other words, and this is a very important point, without a biological *cause* there would be no *development*. This is the clincher. This is why psychosocial factors alone cannot cause addiction in anyone. The person must first be biologically vulnerable to the substance in question, and this holds true for all those with chemical addictions.

This is why it is very unlikely, if not outright impossible, for any person to keep themselves from becoming an addict (short of complete abstinence) – for the one underlying cause, one's individual level of biological vulnerability, is not within human control. For those highly vulnerable (and who do not know this), there really is nothing they can or would do to ward off an addiction until it was too late. For them, by the time their addiction becomes readily apparent, their brains would have already become physically and psychologically altered, resulting in changes in thinking and perceiving that makes it virtually impossible for them to recognize their vulnerability and stop the progression before the addiction has taken a firm hold on them (remember the ten year addictions counselor who fell victim to addiction himself).

BENEFITS

There are good reasons why a complete and comprehensive conceptualization of addiction is needed in the field and it's time for our biological evidence to claim its rightful place among the psycho-emotional and socio-environmental contributing factors of development:

The Benefits of Bio-Vulnerability:

1. It provides a sound explanation for why addicts could not control their use, no matter how hard they might have tried.
2. It provides a sound explanation for why they cannot use like other people.
3. It provides a sound explanation for why they cannot use in the future, no matter how psychologically, emotionally, and/or spiritually healthy they become.
4. It is much easier for addicts to accept, compared to

mental failings or the inability to cope with life-course events.

5. It removes the likelihood of placing the blame of addiction on others, poor luck, and the world at large.

6. It makes it easier for addicts to identify the addiction within themselves. This is because they know in their hearts' that they respond to drugs differently.

7. It does not attack one's self-image, and this helps to distance sufferers from the devastating stigma that is so closely associated with addiction.

8. It provides the potential for full recovery. Rather than being in-recovery for the rest of their lives, they can actually recover.

9. It reduces the potential distance between counselor and client, making it possible to work more closely together and gain better results.

10. It provides a release from all the guilt and shame implied within the psychosocial perspective.

As you can see, there are tremendous benefits that can come from an untainted inclusion of biological vulnerability, and this is a great starting point for anyone suffering from addiction. However, this is also a good time to restate that causation is only a very small part of the whole recovery process. In treatment, biological vulnerability is something that is mostly educational, and must be reinforced throughout the treatment process. Even after cessation (stopping), there is an enormous amount of work in addressing all the psychological and social repercussions of use, and this is another aspect those with addictions have a hard time recognizing and accepting, especially those who have been severely affected.

The main thing to consider here is which perspective you think is most beneficial to one's self-esteem and self-image. Of course there is much more to it than just biological vulnerability, as people also adapt to drug use psychologically and socially, which needs to be addressed in treatment. But if we can eliminate all the guilt and shame associated with and imputed in our current perceptions, it is clear we would be able to provide more humane and effective treatment in the future. Through accepting biological predisposition as the foundational cause of chemical addictions, we will be in an excellent position to intervene much sooner. We can approach those with high and intense reactions to a substance and inform them of their vulnerability anywhere along the progression instead of having to wait until addictions are firmly set and causing severe distress. In other words, we do not have to wait for them to *want* recovery before we can intervene and help them to see this.

Today, we have all the evidence we need to put this biological perspective to use; however, it will only become useful if we can all come together on it. I am not suggesting an acceptance on blind faith, and this is why I wrote this book. This information needs to be implemented into the field and I challenge the profession to put it to the test. Personally, I have applied it to every possible scenario I could come up with and it continues to hold true and explain all the little nuances and mysteries of addiction. Now it is time to convey this understanding to others in the field and challenge their long held beliefs. This is not going to be an easy task at all, but beliefs can and do change.

REVOLUTION –
"A sudden, radical, or complete
change – a fundamental change
in the way of thinking about or
visualizing something"
– Merriam-Webster (2000)

Chapter 16

Epilogue

I realize wrapping our minds around this new way of thinking is going to be hard for most of us. It seems like it goes against all our logic, but this is what appears to have been missing for a very long time. The authors at AA had to adjust their thinking and I know we can, too. Despite the empty claims that causation has nothing to do with treatment, I believe I have adequately dispelled this myth by providing numerous examples to the contrary. There is no doubt that causation has everything to do with treatment. I also believe that if we embrace this new frontier of applied science through the use of our biological evidence and change our thinking, we are going to see some dramatically significant improvements.

One of my colleagues in the field once stated that the cause of addiction was irrelevant because we do not treat the actual cause. However, as I have demonstrated, one's perception of where addiction stems from can easily and inadvertently be implied and insinuated without ever addressing this issue directly. And that perception can, and often does, have a huge impact on the treatment process and its effects on all those afflicted. Perceptions can either help to encourage and support recovery, or they can inadvertently hinder the process.

Although we may never be able to claim with absolute fact, that we know exactly where addictions stem from (the cause of genetic randomization), just like we may never be able to claim we know exactly where cancer stems from, this does not mean we will not form an opinion on it; and that this opinion will have its effects on the clients we serve. When we hear of a person with lung cancer, the first thing we want to know is whether or not they smoked cigarettes. When we are told they never smoked, we are dumbfounded. It is as if we want to blame someone or something. We want answers, even when there are none. What we may actually be looking for is confirmation that we are still in control of our own destiny; when the answers are elusive, it scares the hell out of us. This is probably why the psychosocial perspective *of causation*, with all its practical deficits, is so hard to combat.

People do not want to give up their control, and this is exactly what the biological perspective of genetic predisposition is requiring – the realization that no one who uses a psychotropic substance has any real control over addiction. The biological perspective of causation clearly promises to be much more effective but are we willing to pay the price for it, the price of forfeiting our claim of control? At this point in time, the choice of whether to adopt this biological perspective is really up to the provider. One cannot hang on the fence between these two perspectives because underlying beliefs will continue to affect and impact treatment whether they are acknowledged or not. *If we are applying treatment, we must know where we stand.*

Applying the biological perspective to treatment does not mean that psychosocial issues do not apply. They are still a huge part of treatment. The psychosocial perspective is needed to address all the underlying emotional, psychological, and social ills present in those afflicted. This is what all our current therapies were developed for, not addiction. Clients do play a significant role in creating and maintaining their psychological, emotional, and social problems; however, in addressing these issues, it should be made perfectly clear that although these factors have contributed heavily to the continuation of use in the *development* of addiction, they cannot *cause* addiction – not without some degree or level of biological vulnerability to a specific substance. The blame really needs to be put back on the drug and the individual's biological response.

If we accept the perception that biological vulnerability is the indisputable foundation of all chemical addictions, we would clearly see that it is actually the chemical that "chooses" the addict, rather than the addict choosing the chemical.

Scientific evidence continues to reveal and support that chemical addictions stem from unavoidable biological reactions, but this information has not been fully understood, accepted, or applied in the field. It appears to have been unintentionally altered to conform to the beliefs of the majority who unwittingly adhere to the psychosocial perspective. This is the perspective that continues to prevail, and in many ways may actually be hindering the potential for progress in recovery for many patients. This may be the result of many factors; e.g., inappropriate motivational tactics, the fear of releasing patients from causal responsibility, personal experience with psychotropic drugs and the misinterpretation of information.

The biopsychosocial factors of addiction are the visible tumors of addiction that are treatable; they are not necessarily the cause. When we take a look at some powerfully addictive drugs like heroin and nicotine, it is quite easy to see how drugs can actually cause the psychological and social adaptations or dependencies present in those afflicted. Thus, whether or not biological causation is accepted by everyone in the field, we can still change how we perceive the condition; and therefore, how we go about treating it.

I also think it is important to recognize chemical addictions as being distinctively different from process addictions, such as gambling or sex addictions, which are actually obsessions. Even though both consist of compulsive behavior, process addictions are only driven by a mental obsession, whereas chemical addictions are driven by the action of chemicals on the brain, leading to the mental obsession to use. In other words, the reasoning or forces behind these obsessions are different. Chemical addictions are not merely psycho-emotional behavioral problems; they are driven by the *effects* of drugs on the pleasure center of the brain, which should be made abundantly clear to those afflicted. Addiction is the result of a chemical reaction, and this is an extremely important aspect of the condition for those with addictions to learn, accept, and understand; it can give them the strength they will need to stand against the incredibly strong urges and temptations they are bound to face. It can be their foundation on which to build a solid, unwavering, and permanent recovery.

Understanding biological predisposition relieves years and years of guilt and shame present in those afflicted. It can also help to renew one's self confidence (and self-concept) in their ability to face life's challenges without using. It has been shown to provide the motivation necessary for addicts to take responsibility for having the condition, not for causing it, and to address all their psychosocial dependencies that have developed as a result. This has been made evident through the success of AA over the past 80 years or so, in which they referred to biological predisposition as some type of allergy.

This issue of causation may appear to be just one of the many issues involved in treatment, but as you can see, it is not just one issue because it affects so many different aspects of treatment. I am not alone in believing that biological vulnerability is the basis or foundational cause of all chemical addictions. The epigenetic concept of disease also supports this as the most likely cause of addiction, and it may just provide us with what is needed to help patients achieve the three main **Goals of Treatment:**

1. Maintain abstinence by overcoming the desire-to-use.
2. Repair physical and psycho-emotional damage from use.
3. Develop a personality and character strong enough to withstand challenges and enjoy life without using.

When it comes to the matter of belief, it is a personal choice. One can believe the myth that everyone is just as biologically vulnerable to addiction as the next person, or, they can believe only those with greater degrees of bio-vulnerability can fall victim to chemical addictions. It's that simple. This simple twist of belief may be all that is needed to turn treatment around and put the brakes on readmissions – the revolving door of treatment. The big difference here lies in how well each of these two perspectives work in real practice. Which one provides better effectiveness? There are obviously some very significant problems with the psychosocial perspective, and the biological perspective has not been put to the test. However, is there really any danger in adopting a view that holds the potential to be much more effective?

Changing a majority view about something may not be easy, but it is possible. For example, back in the days of slavery, millions of Whites were convinced that they were more intelligent than the Black people they put into slavery (probably as a means to justify their support of this horrid practice, and still be at peace with themselves). To support this idea, the African culture appeared to be barbaric in relation to the White "civilized" world, and since Black slaves lacked any type of formal education (and were not given any), they must have surely been less intelligent. And, to top it off, a picture of a larger White brain appeared in print all over America and Europe. As a result, there existed such a belief, so ingrained into the minds of White people all over the world that it appeared nothing could ever change it. After all, who could dare argue with all this "common sense?" It took time, but this belief has perished – *the truth prevailed.* Change, even against the belief of the majority, is possible. This is the call of this book. Yes, the observable differences are obvious. Alcohol and drug users surely appear to be doing this to themselves, but is this the undeniable truth? I think not; the evidence is telling us a whole different story.

As you can see, beliefs are often incorrect and highly infectious. And, for the most part, and despite evidence to the contrary, people will believe whatever it is they *want* to believe. This may explain why the stigma of addiction, which appears to be the belief and consensus of the majority, continues to thrive in our society, both in and out of treatment. However, whether addicts cause their own addictions or not is not even the real issue here. The real issue is which perspective is more effective and useful for those in need. If history can teach us anything, it is that the concept of biological predisposition has been very successful in helping millions of alcoholics in AA recognize, accept, and address their condition for over 80 years. So, as you can see, it really comes down to a matter of belief. In order to best help others fight off their addiction, might we first have to question and fight off our own ancient beliefs?

This book is not about proving either perspective right or wrong, for all three bio-psycho-social factors play a role in the development of chemical addictions. This is not a question. What is falling under scrutiny here is how much value, weight, or credence each provider gives to the biological factors in light of our newly found and growing evidence.

Having studied the phenomenon of chemical addictions for the past 20 years, I feel responsible to share what I found with others. I want to let addicts know that they do not have to sink to such low levels of despair before they can be helped. I believe we can stop the revolving door of treatment by the way addiction is perceived, and by applying a more comprehensive understanding of the biological perspective to our current treatment methods. If nothing changes, nothing changes; however, I believe there is always room for improvement. Through the growing acceptance of our biological evidence we are bound to see drastic changes in the field; however, it must start with each and every one of us on an individual basis.

Other than having a biological vulnerability to a chemical substance, addicts are really no different than any one of us, and this is what biological predisposition allows us to see. Even Abraham Lincoln saw this. Yes, most of them are likely to be suffering from a plethora of psychological and social ills as a result of their addiction, especially while they are recovering, but who wouldn't after years and years of having to adapt to the call of a drug, not to mention having to accept such a disgraceful, stigmatized, and dehumanizing condition before they can be helped. This is why the knowledge of a foundational cause of addiction is so vitally important; not that this knowledge itself would do anything, but in all the ways this simple twist of belief can benefit all those in need (Benefits of Bio-vulnerability).

Therefore, we need to get everyone on board with this new perspective if we are ever going to make any real progress in the overall treatment of chemical addictions. Deep in the heart and soul of every addict, they instinctively know they did nothing wrong. They used like they did because it came so very natural to them – there is no other reason. The monkey experiments in Oregon, along with all the other experiments over the past few decades, have confirmed this. The addicts' only mistake was not to accept a condition they had no way of knowing they had; and, unless our professionals in the field start to acknowledge this and challenge their own beliefs, nothing will change.

What I am offering here is a belief. A belief based on science, not assumptions or myths. For example, it is perfectly okay to have weak bones, as long as one treads softly and is aware of their condition. Rock climbing is not for those with weak bones, just as drug use is not for those who get sucked into its powerfully strong and luring effects. In other words, I am offering a more effective way to perceive, understand, and address chemical addictions. This is what all the research is leading us towards when we look at it through the big picture. I can envision great strides ahead if we do not let our old antiquated beliefs stand in the way of progress. When it is all said and done, _every recovery is built on belief_, and if we can support a belief that is based on science and proves to be more effective in the long run, on a large scale basis, then we are headed somewhere exciting. We are headed toward a new and more effective era of treatment and prevention.

Therefore, the challenge I present to everyone reading this book is to question everything in it; to ponder upon its contents. Repetition is one way to learn, which I have tried to incorporate throughout this book, but real learning comes through giving thought to what has been written. So, this is my plea to you. Beat up everything I have laid down here; chew it up, challenge it, discuss it, and digest it. This is how we learn. It is not enough to read it and put it down, not when it comes to beliefs. And, this is what I am asking of each and every one of you, to challenge and question your own beliefs.

Thank you for giving me your time and attention, and I hope I have given you something of value in return. The information I have presented here comes from 10 years of collegiate study (240 credit hours), a thorough review and examination of innumerous studies, experiments, and literature; knowledge of commonly used and accepted practices and beliefs; current theories, personal observations, and personal interviews. In doing so, I believe I have provided a clear picture of addiction, treatment, and recovery.

I realize this is by no means the end all, but I do hope it is a good start. My goal is not to end any disputes here, but to help and encourage others in the field to question their beliefs and seek out more effective ways to use and apply our biological evidence. There are a lot of great, creative, and intelligent people out there who can take this to the next level and my prayers are with them all.

In closing, I would like to leave you with this one last thought from Larson to ponder:

> A man is walking beside a river and notices that someone is drowning. He jumps in, pulls the person to shore and revives him. Then another drowning person calls for help, and again the man successfully rescues him. As the man is about to walk away, a passerby shouts, 'Hey, there's another person drowning out there! Where are you going?' The man replies, 'I'm going upstream to see who's throwing all these people in!' (Larson, 1993, pp. 79-80; from Walsh-Burke, 2006, p. 101).

So, please join me on this venture as we travel upstream, armed with all our new scientific knowledge, in the quest to eradicate the stigma of addiction and put an end to the revolving door of treatment. Just like the addict who is caught in the grips of their addiction must eventually realize that what they are doing does not work, and has to accept it and seek change, so too must the field of treatment, especially if what is being done is part of the problem. Haven't we been pulling the drowning from rough waters long enough, only to see them fall right back in? Today we have all the evidence and knowledge we need to turn this around, so let's take it upstream to stop the flow, or at least slow it down a little. All we have to do is pick up what has been laid at our feet and put it to use. With all our new clinical and scientific advancements being made, I have no doubt the 21st Century will mark the turning point in how people view and address chemical addictions from now on.

Please join with me on this quest to usher in this all new and amazing era of treatment. We are looking upon a new horizon, a new frontier! Welcome aboard!

Thank you –
Adam McArnold

Special Thanks

I would like to take this opportunity to send out a special thank you to all the wonderful clients, professors, counselors, therapists, and colleagues I have had the pleasure to work with and get to know along the way. These are the people who unwittingly inspired me to sit down and write this book and my life has been greatly enriched and blessed to have known them. I would also like to thank my family and children for all their love, support, and patience while I undertook this most worthwhile project.

References

Addiction and Recovery: The Jellinek Curve [PDF]. (n.d.). Retrieved from http://www.in.gov/judiciary/ijlap/docs/ jellinek.pdf

Alcoholics Anonymous World Services Inc. (1976). *Alcoholics Anonymous* (3rded.). New York, NY: A.A. World Services Inc.

Alcoholics Anonymous World Services Inc. (2001). *Alcoholics Anonymous* (4thed.). New York, NY: A.A. World Services Inc.

Alcoholism - Is it Inherited? (n.d.). Retrieved 6/23/10 from: http://alcoholism.about.com/library/weekly/aa990517.htm

American Psychiatric Association (2000). *Diagnostic and Statistical Manual of Mental Disorders, fourth edition, text revision* (DSM-IV-TR). Washington, DC: American Psychiatric Association

American Psychiatric Association (2013). *Diagnostic and Statistical Manual of Mental Disorders, fifth edition,* (DSM-5). Washington, DC: American Psychiatric Association

American Psychological Association (n.d.). Psychology topics/ Addictions. Retrieved 1/12/15 from: http://www.apa.org/ topics/addiction/

ASAM: American Society of Addiction Medicine (n.d.). For the public/Definition of addiction [website]. Retrieved 1/12/15 from: http://www.asam.org/for-the-public/definition-of-addiction

Bland, J. (2008). Speaking at Nutri Seminar in London (Video). Retrieved 5/10/2011 from: http://youtu.be/fOgk9GefR0c

Bland, J. (2011). An Interview with Dr. Jeffery Bland at the 2011 Integrative Healthcare Symposium in NYC (Video). Retrieved 5/10/2011 from: http://youtu.be/cEuoFLN-4zhE

Brady, K. T. & Sonne, S. C. (1999). The role of stress in alcohol use, alcoholism, treatment, and relapse. *Alcohol Research and Health* 23(4), 263-271

Brickman, P., Rabinowitz, V. C., Karuza, J. Jr., Coates, D., Chon, E., & Kidder, L. (1982). Models of helping and coping. *American Psychologist,* 37(4), 368-384.

Bridges, W. (2004). *Transitions: Making Sense of Life's Changes.* Cambridge, MA: Da Capo Press; Perseus Books Group

Brown, N. (2004). *Psychoeducational Groups: Process and Practice.* New York, NY: Brunner-Routledge.

Burkhalter, P. (1975). *Nursing care of the alcoholic and drug abuser.* New York, NY: McGraw-Hill, Inc.

Burrow-Sanchez, J. & Hawken, L. (2007). *Helping Students Overcome Substance Abuse.* New York, NY: Guilford Press.

Chang, V., Scott, S. & Decker, C. (2009). *Developing Helping Skills: A Step by Step Approach.* Belmont, CA: Brooks/Cole.

Cognitive Behavior.Com (n.d.). The Cognitive Behavior Management Reference (website). Retrieved 7/8/11 from http://www.cognitivebehavior.com/

Corey, M. S. & Corey, G. (2006). *Groups: Process and Practice* (7thed.). Belmont, CA: Brooks/Cole.

Corey, M., Corey, G. & Corey, C. (2010). *Groups: Process and Practice* (8thed.). Belmont, CA: Brooks/Cole.

Corsini, R. J. & Wedding, D. (2008). *Current Psychotherapies* (8thed.). Belmont, CA: Thomson Brooks/Cole.

Cubic, B. A. (2008). *Introduction to current psychotherapies* [Power Point slides]. Belmont, CA: Thomson Brooks/Cole.

Deffenbacher, J. L. (2011). Cognitive-behavioral conceptualization and treatment of anger. *Cognitive and Behavioral Practice* (18), 212-221

Ellinwood, E. & Kilbey, M. (1977). *Cocaine and other stimulants* (Volume 21 of the series: *Advances in behavioral biology*). New York, NY: Plenum Press. 481-482

Epigenetics: How Does it Work? (2008). A video by Dr. Joseph Mercola. Retrieved 5/10/2011 from: http://www.youtube.com/watch?v=Y-Hh7b3Nxxc

Fonda, J. (2009). The disease model of addiction (website). Retrieved 7/25/15 from: http://www.groundreport.com/the-disease-model-of-addiction/

Friedman, R. A. (2011). Who falls to addiction, and who is unscathed? *The New York Times*: Health [website]. Retrieved 8/2/11 from: http://www.nytimes. com/2011/08/02/health/02abuse.html?_r=1&smid=fb-nytimeshealth

Gaylin, W. (2001). *How Psychotherapy Really Works: How it Works When it Works and Why Sometimes It Doesn't.* New York, NY: McGraw-Hill.

Gitlow, S. (2013). Commentary: DSM-5: New addiction terminology, same disease (website). *Drugfree.org/Join-Together.* Retrieved 7/15/2014 from: http://www.drugfree. org/join-together/addiction/commentary-dsm-5-new-addiction-terminology-same-disease?utm_source=Join%20 Together%20Weekly&utm_campaign=f5004a3b2c-JTWN_DSM5_NewAddictnTerminologySameDisease06 0713&utm_medium=email&utm_term=0_0a25dfa1a1-f5004a3b2c-221452561

Goodwin, D. (1988). *Is alcoholism hereditary* (2nded.). New York, NY: Ballantine Books (pp. 27, 136)

Harris, Thomas A. *I'm OK, You're OK: A Practical Guide to Transactional Analysis.* New York: Harper & Row, 1969.

HBO Documentary Films (2007). *Addiction: Why can't they just stop?* Home Box Office Inc. [website] http://www.hbo. com/addiction/

IUSM News Room (2014). Panel of 11 genes predicts alcoholism risk, gives new insights into biology of the disease (website). *Indiana University School of Medicine.* Retrieved 7/20/15 from: http://news.medicine.iu.edu/releases/2014/05/genes-predict-alcoholism.shtml

Kinney, J. & Leaton, G. (1991). *Loosening the grip* (4thed.). St. Louis, MO: Mosby-Year Book, Inc.

Kuhar, M. (2012). *The Addicted Brain: Why We Abuse Drugs, Alcohol, and Nicotine.* Upper Saddle River, NJ: Pearson Education Inc.

McCauley. K. (2012). Pleasure Unwoven (DVD). The Institute for Addiction Study (website). http://www.institute-foraddictionstudy.com/products.html

McKay, M. (1992). *Focal Group Psychotherapy.* Oakland, CA: New Harbinger Publications.

Merriam-Webster's Collegiate Dictionary & Thesaurus. (2000). Deluxe Audio Edition [CD-ROM]. Fogware Publishing

Merriam-Webster's Online Dictionary (n.d.). Addiction. Retrieved 01/12/15 from: http://www.merriam-webster. com/dictionary/addiction

Miller, W. R. & Rollnick, S. (2002). *Motivational Interviewing: Preparing People for Change* (2nded.). New York, NY: The Guilford Press.

Mitcheson, L., Maslin, J., Meynen, T., Morrison, T., Hill, R., Wanigaratne, S., &Padesky, C., (2010). *Applied cognitive and behavioural approaches to the treatment of addiction: A practical treatment guide.* West Sussex, UK: Wiley-Blackwell Publishing

Monkey See, Monkey Do. (2011). [TV segment on 20/20 called Mother's Day Murder, Season 31, 1/21/2011]. Retrieved 5/10/11 from: http://abc.go.com/ watch/2020/166626

National Institute on Alcohol Abuse and Alcoholism (2000).

Alcohol Alert [Publication No.48]. http://www.niaaa.nih.
gov/publications/aa48.htm

National Institute on Alcohol Abuse and Alcoholism (2003).
Frequently Asked Questions (website). http://www.niaaa.
nih.gov/faq/q-a.htm

Neukrug, E. S. (2008). *Theories in action* [DVD]. Belmont,
CA: Brooks/Cole.

NIAAA, National Institute on Alcohol Abuse and Addiction
(n.d.). National Institute of Health: NIH News (website).
Retrieved 7/3/11 from: http://www.niaaa.nih.gov/News-
Events/NewsReleases/stress-induced.htm

NIDA, National Institute on Drug Abuse (2010). Media
guide/The Science of Drug Abuse and Addiction: The Basics. Retrieved 4/30/14 from: http://www.drugabuse.gov/
publications/media-guide/science-drug-abuse-addiction

NIDA, National Institute on Drug Abuse (n.d.). NIDA
Community Drug Alert Bulletin: Stress and Substance
Abuse (website). Retrieved 7/3/11 from http://archives.
drugabuse.gov/stressalert/StressAlert.html

O'Donohue, W. & Fisher, J. (2008). *Cognitive Behavior
Therapy: Applying Empirically Supported Techniques in Your
Practice.* Hoboken, NJ: John Wiley and Son Inc.

OMG/ Yahoo (2011). Russell Brand Pens Touching Tribute
to Amy Winehouse. Retrieved 7/30/11 from http://omg.
yahoo.com/news/russell-brand-pens-touching-tribute-to-
amy-winehouse/67927

Opioids' Side Effects and Risk of Addiction Related to Genetics, Twin Study Finds (2012). The Partnership at Drug-
free.org; Join Together. Retrieved 7/24/15 from: http://

References

www.drugfree.org/join-together/opioids-side-effects-and-risk-of-addiction-related-to-genetics-twin-study-finds/ Overview of Models of Addiction (n.d.). Family studies (p. 4). Retrieved 6/16/13 from: http://www.elearnportal. com/courses/psychology/psychology-of-addictions/psychology-of-addictions-overview-of-models-of-addiction

Peroutka, S. J. (1990). *Ecstasy*. Dordrecht, Netherlands: Kluwer Academic Publishers. p.10

Pita, D. D. & Spaniol, L. R. J. (2002). *A Comprehensive Guide for Integrated Treatment of People with Co-occurring Disorders*. Boston, MA: Center for Psychiatric Rehabilitation, Boston University.

Pleasure Unwoven (DVD). Offered by the Institute for Addiction Study. http://www.instituteforaddictionstudy. com/products.html

Prochaska, J.O. & DiClemente, C.C. (1984). *The transtheoretical approach: Crossing transitional boundaries of therapy*. Homewood, IL: Dow Jones-Irwin

Psychiatry Research (2015). Deepen your understanding of alcohol use disorders - Part One: The Addicted Brain (Webinar). *Elsevier*. Retrieved 8/13/15 from: http:// progressinmind.elsevierresource.com/webinar/deepen-your-understanding-alcohol-use-disorders-part-1?utm_source=newsletter &utm_medium=email&utm_content=%20&utm_campaign=early-recognition

Psychology Today (n.d.). Basics/Addiction. Retrieved 1/12/15 from: http://www.psychologytoday.com/basics/addiction

Quenqua, D. (2011). Rethinking addiction's roots, and its treatment. The New York Times: Health (web-

site). Retrieved 7/30/11 from: http://www.nytimes.
com/2011/07/11/health/11addictions.html?_r=1

Researchers ID Genetic Markers for Nicotine Addiction
(2010). The Partnership at Drugfree.org; Join Together.
Retrieved 7/24/15 from: http://www.drugfree.org/join-
together/researchers-id-genetic-markers-for-nicotine-
addiction-2/

Rosellini, Gayle & Worden, Mark (1997). *The anger test, of
course you're angry: A guide to dealing with the emotions of
substance abuse.* Center City, MN: Hazelton Foundation
retrieved 6/3/11 from: http://www.mentalhelp.net/poc/
view_doc.php?type=doc&id=3396&cn=116

Rubin, S. E. & Roessler, R. T. (2008). *Foundations of the Voca-
tional Rehabilitation Process* (6thed.). Austin, TX: Pro-Ed

Salzberg, S. (2011). *Real Happiness: The Power of Meditation.*
New York, NY: Workman Publishing Company, Inc.

Sander, R. S. (2009). *Thinking Simply About Addiction: A
Handbook for Recovery.* New York: Penguin Group Inc.

Schaef, A. W. (1987). When Society Becomes an Addict. New
York, NY; Harper Collins Publishers.

Schuckit, M. A., Kalmijn, J. A., Smith, T. L., Saunders, G. &
Fromme, K. (2012). Structuring a college alcohol prevention program on the low level of response to alcohol
model: A pilot study. *Alcoholism: Clinical and Experimental Research* 36(7) 1244-1252. DOI: 10.1111/j.1530-
0277.2011.01723.x

Spitzer, R. L., First, M. B., Williams, J. B. & Gibbon, M.
(2006). *DSM-IV-TR Case Book, Volume 2: Experts tell how
they treated their patients.* Arlington, VA: American Psychi-

atric Publishing

Spokane County Mental Health (n.d.). Stages of Change: A Process to Understand How We Approach Recovery From Addiction [PDF]. Retrieved 5/3/2011 from: http://www. spokanecounty.org/MentalHealth/Data/Gain-Adult/Stages%20of%20Change/stagesofchange_000.pdf

Stocker, S. & NIDA NOTES (1998). Men and women in drug abuse treatment relapse at different rates and for different reasons. *NIDA: The Science of Drug Abuse & Addiction 13*(4). Retrieved 7/3/11 from: http://archives.ddrugabuse.gov/NIDA_Notes/NNVol13N4/Relapse.html

Study Finds More Evidence of Genetic Predisposition to Alcoholism (2007). The Partnership at Drugfree.org; Join Together. Retrieved 7/24/15 from: http://www.drugfree. org/join-together/study-finds-more-evidence-of-genetic-predisposition-to-alcoholism/

Taylor, C. R., Lillis, C., LeMone, P. & Lynn, P. (2008). Fundamentals of Nursing: The Art and Science of Nursing Care (6thed.). Philadelphia, PA: Walters Kluwer/ Lippincott Williams & Wilkins

The Alcohol Use Disorders Identification Test (n.d.). Retrieved 7/1/11 from: http://www.assessmentgenerator. com/H/cRMaven0071131762524.html

The Coping Skills Test at Coach for Outcomes (n.d.). Retrieved 6/30/11 from: http://www.assessmentgenerator. com/H/cRMaven0071131762524.htmlted

Thombs, D. L. (1999). *Introduction to Addictive Behaviors* (2nded.). New York, NY: The Guilford Press

Van Sickle, R. (1996). Peace of Body, Peace of Mind: Practical, Effective Techniques for Mental fitness (website). Retrieved 7/5/11 from: http://www.pljunlimited.com/

Volkow, N. (n.d.). An Interview with neuroscientist in charge of the *National Institute on Drug Abuse*, who also happens to be the great-granddaughter of Leon Trotsky. New York Times [video]. Retrieved 7/30/11 from: http://video.nytimes.com/video/2011/06/13/science/100000000862646/nora-volkow.html?ref=health

Volkow, N. (n.d.). The Science of Addiction: Drug Abuse and Addiction. National Institute on Drug Abuse [NIH Pub no. 07-5605, 2008]. Retrieved 7/12/2010 from http://www.nida.nih.gov/scienceofaddiction/addiction.html

Walsh-Burke, K. (2006). *Grief and loss: Theories and skills for helping professionals.* Boston, MA: Pearson Education, Inc.

Wilson-Schaef, A. (1987). *When society becomes an addict.* New York, NY: Harper Collins Publishers, Inc.

Yalom, I.D. (1985). *The Theory and Practice of Group Psychotherapy* (3rded.). New York, NY: Basic Books, Inc.

Yalom, I.D. & Leszcz, M. (2005). *The Theory and Practice of Group Psychotherapy* (5thed.). New York, NY: Basic Books

YouTube (2010). The Power of Words [video]. Retrieved 7/5/11 from: http://www.youtube.com/results?search_query=the+power+of+words&aq=f

About the Author

❦

Adam McArnold, MS, CRC, CASAC, MHC, is an addictions counselor who lives in Upstate New York. He has
over twenty years of experience in chemical addictions. He
obtained his Bachelor's Degree in Health Science from The
State University of New York where he majored in Substance
Abuse Counseling. From there he spent an additional two years
studying the anatomy and physiology of the human body to
gain a better understanding of the genetic and biological components of addiction. Upon completion of those six years, he
continued on for a Master's Degree in Rehabilitation Counseling. Enlightened by what he had learned about addictions in
that program, he dove back into his study and investigation of
chemical addictions with a renewed enthusiasm for answers,
all while completing an advanced graduate program in Mental
Health Counseling.

Throughout the years, Adam has had the opportunity to study residential, inpatient, and outpatient treatment modalities, all of which appear to fail miserably in providing any real measure of success in the treatment of chemical addictions. Finding this realization extremely disturbing, he started to re-examine all the research he had studied over his ten years of collegiate education, and before he knew it, a more comprehensive view of addiction started to materialize; a conceptualization based on the plain fact that psychotropic substances affect and impact everyone a little differently; a fact, although well-accepted and accounted for in the administration of pharmaceutical medications, is not even a consideration when it comes to treating and making sense of addictions. Having applied this understanding, Adam soon realized how effective it was. As a result, he knew what he had to do – pass it on.

Made in the USA
Middletown, DE
19 February 2020